START YOUR DAY AWESOME

· with british jumbo oats, low fat yoghurt & real fruit ·

Available in selected stores·

*Subject to availability.

CONTENTS

LUNCH

DINNER

BREAKFAST

FEATURES

LIGHT MEALS

SMOOTHIES

Men's Fitness magazine

30 MINUTE FITNESS MEALS

By Ben Ince

Art Director Rob Lavery

Photography Lauren Mclean, Danny Bird, Henry Carter, packshotfactory.co.uk

Food styling Karol Gladki, Rob Lavery

Chief Subeditor Jo Williams

Additional photography iStock

Men's Fitness

Art Director Ped Millichamp

Managing Editor Chris Miller

Editor Joel Snape

MAGBOOK

Group Publisher **Russell Blackman**
Associate Publisher **Nicola Bates**
Group Publishing Director **James Burnay**
Group Managing Director **Ian Westwood**
International Business Development Director
Dharmesh Mistry
Digital Production Manager **Nicky Baker**
Operations Director **Robin Ryan**
Managing Director of Advertising
Julian Lloyd-Evans
Newstrade Director **David Barker**
Chief Operating Officer/
Chief Financial Officer **Brett Reynolds**
Group Finance Director **Ian Leggett**
Chief Executive Officer **James Tye**
Company Founder **Felix Dennis**

The 'MagBook' brand is a trademark of Dennis Publishing Ltd,
30 Cleveland Street, London W1T 4JD.
Company registered in England.
All material © 2015 Dennis Publishing Ltd. All rights reserved.
Men's Fitness is a trademark of Felix Dennis and may not be
used or reproduced in whole or part without the
consent of the publishers. Printed by Sterling Press Ltd.

30-MINUTE FITNESS MEALS ISBN **1-78106-432-6**
To license this product please contact Nicole Adams on
+44 (0) 20 7907 6134 or nicole_adams@dennis.co.uk

Advertising
Rick Asiyani rick_asiyani@dennis.co.uk

To subscribe to *Men's Fitness* magazine,
call **0844 844 0081** or go to **mensfitness.co.uk**

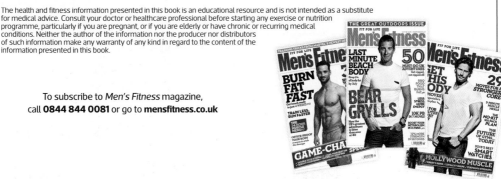

EAT BETTER, LOOK BETTER

BEN INCE, EDITOR

How many times have you heard someone use the excuse 'I don't have time to cook' to justify making poor food choices? It's easily done – especially given the abundance of tempting ready meals lining the aisles of our supermarkets.

But here's the truth: healthy eating really doesn't need to be time consuming or complicated. All the recipes in this book can be prepared in just 30 minutes or less, allowing even the most time-poor individual to enjoy delicious, home-cooked food without having to resort to takeaways and microwaveable meals.

Whether you want to build muscle, burn fat or just live a generally healthy lifestyle, what you do in this kitchen is just as important as the time you spend in the gym, so we've made sure all these recipes feature key nutrients to help you achieve your fitness goals.

So read on, grab your chef's hat and get stuck in. Your journey to healthier eating starts here.

LEAD. *DON'T FOLLOW*

We've spent years developing inhouse manufacturing that allows us to incorporate **the very best ingredients** to make unique market leading products.

WHEY REFRESH®

Our hugely popular protein drink containing **30 g of protein from whey isolate**, zero fat and zero carbohydrate per bottle.

Whey Refresh® is the perfect product for people who demand a convenient source of high quality protein. It is naturally loaded with BCAA's, free from artificial colours, flavours and sweeteners and is virtually free from fat and carbohydrates.

30 g PROTEIN   **ZERO** FAT   **ZERO** CARBOHYDRATE

PER 500 ml BOTTLE

INSTANT WHEY™ PRO

Finding a whey protein that balances unsurpassed quality with a great taste and health considerations incorporated into the formulation isn't always easy.

Instant Whey™ PRO delivers a high level of protein at 80% where the main ingredients include whey isolate which has an unchallenged reputation. This isolate incorporates native whey, which is made using a process that keeps far more of the important amino acids in place. This makes it perfect for aiding muscle recovery after strenuous exercise or gym workouts.

Furthermore, it includes 500 million spores of friendly bacteria per serving and DigeZyme® Enzyme complex.

20 g PROTEIN   ONLY 92 CALORIES   ONLY 1.1g FAT

PER 25 g SERVING

TOMORROW'S NUTRITION TODAY™

NUTRITION 101

Follow these simple guidelines that will help you eat better, train harder, store less fat and build more muscle

1

STICK TO WHOLEFOODS

Nothing will hamper your progress more than over-indulging in processed foods. Regularly eating the refined carbs and sugars that form the basis of most processed snacks, baked goods and fast foods will sap your energy levels and cause fat-storing blood sugar spikes, making it far harder to lose weight or perform at an optimum level. To make matters worse, these foods typically contain high levels of man-made trans fats, which will make you feel even more lethargic and boost your levels of 'bad' LDL cholesterol.

For a healthier alternative, swap processed foods for more naturally indulgent wholefood alternatives. For example, you can trade crisps for nuts, chocolate spread for peanut butter and breakfast cereal for porridge oats, all of which have additional nutritional benefits.

2 EAT MORE VEG THAN FRUIT

All fruits and veg contain health-enhancing nutrients. But while the five-a-day mantra is good at encouraging people to eat more fresh produce in general, if you want to get the most out of your training and support your fat-burning and muscle-building efforts, you need to be a lot more specific about your intake.

For a start, try to have as much veg as possible while cutting back on fruit. Fruit is high in fructose, a type of sugar that plays havoc with blood sugar levels, making you far more likely to store fat. Vegetables, on the other hand, contain no fructose but are just as nutrient dense, making them a far better dietary staple. Green vegetables in particular are a great choice – they're an excellent source of slow-release carbs, unlike starchy root vegetables such as potatoes, which can also negatively affect your blood sugar levels.

Eat as many servings of green vegetables as possible each day and limit your fruit intake to one to two servings, ideally from low-sugar sources such as blueberries or strawberries.

No ordinary protein shake.

Used by celebrities and athletes, Twist is a delicious blend of full flavoured Colombian Coffee and Whey Protein Isolate in a convenient bottle – Just add water and shake! 90 Calories, 17 grams of Protein, 4.9g Carbohydrates, 0.7g of Sugar and 73mg Caffeine per bottle.

TWIST. *The Coffee Lovers Protein Drink*™

 **twistdrinks**
www.twistdrinks.co.uk

UP YOUR PROTEIN INTAKE

Protein plays a crucial role in building muscle, but it's easy to underestimate just how much you need to maximise its benefits. Estimates vary from 1-4g per kilo of bodyweight per day, but most nutritionists agree that 2g is the minimum. If you want to keep things simple, aim to eat a 20-25g serving of protein – good sources of which include meat, fish, dairy and eggs – with every meal including breakfast, adding an extra post-workout serving on training days.

Sooner or later, someone will probably raise an eyebrow at the amount of protein you're ingesting. They may even tell you it's bad for your health. But the only studies that have suggested protein can cause kidney problems were carried out on people with pre-existing kidney problems. In addition to aiding your muscle-building efforts, protein-rich foods also tend to be very filling, so you avoid the urge to pig out between meals.

4 CHOOSE THE RIGHT FATS

'Eating fatty foods makes you fat' may sound like a logical assumption, but it's a bit more complicated than that. It is true that at nine calories per gram, fat is more calorific than carbohydrate or protein – which contain four each – but the reality is certain fats are a crucial part of your diet. The mono- and polyunsaturated fats that occur naturally in foods such as oily fish, nuts, seeds, olives and coconut oil, for example, play key roles in boosting metabolism, improving hormone synthesis and increasing 'good' HDL cholesterol.

Don't be fooled by 'low-fat' options either. Most have been highly processed to remove the fat, and tend to be packed with salt and sugar to enhance their flavour. Instead, focus your energies on avoiding processed junk foods, high in unhealthy man-made trans fats, and enjoy daily servings of healthy, naturally occurring fat sources.

5 DON'T COUNT CALORIES

It's easy to fall into the trap of focusing on the quantity of calories you're consuming, especially if you're trying to lose weight. But the quality of the food you're eating is far more important, because calories alone don't provide a reliable indication of the effect a food can have on your metabolism. For example, drinking a can of blood sugar-spiking fizzy pop is far more damaging to your fat-loss efforts than eating two protein-rich poached eggs, even though both contain a similar number of calories. It's also easy to use calorie counting as an excuse to justify poor food choices – a 'healthy option' packet of crisps may contain fewer than 100 calories, but it's likely to be full of trans-fats and other nasties. Instead of getting hung up on how many calories every item of food contains, concentrate on eating plenty of wholefoods, vegetables, meats and fish.

6 LOSE THE BOOZE

It may sound obvious, but cutting your alcohol intake will have a huge impact on your attempts to build fat and burn muscle. As well as providing hundreds of nutritionally empty calories, regular boozing stimulates your appetite when you're at your weakest – would you find a doner kebab appealing otherwise? You're also far less likely to want to train or eat healthily when hungover.

If you must indulge, opt for red wine, which has been found to reduce the risk of cardiovascular disease and enhance muscle endurance thanks to its resveratrol content. Stick to two glasses, after which the negatives outweigh the positives.

BREAKFAST

Whether you're trying to burn fat, build muscle or just live a generally healthier life, it pays to start the day as you mean to continue it and enjoy a nutrient-rich meal

FULL ENGLISH BREAKFAST

The fry-up is a great British tradition, but it's hardly the most nutritionally balanced start to the day – unless you go for our enhanced version

INGREDIENTS

(SERVES 1)

2 eggs

1tbsp butter or coconut oil

1 tomato, halved

2 sausages

2 rashers of bacon

1 avocado, sliced

TO MAKE

- Scramble the eggs in the butter or coconut oil, stirring until there's just a little liquid in the pan, then remove from the heat.
- Grill the tomatoes and sausages, and fry the bacon.
- Serve with the avocado and, preferably, black coffee.

Per portion Calories **765** / Protein **33g** / Fat **75g** / Carbs **22g**

THE BENEFITS

TOMATO
provides vitamin C, which boosts immunity.

AVOCADO
provides monounsaturated fat to improve heart health.

BACON
provides zinc, which aids muscle growth.

SCRAMBLED EGGS WITH RICOTTA

Short on time? Toughen up fast with this simple breakfast recipe packed with bone-strengthening spinach and amino acid-packed ricotta

INGREDIENTS

(SERVES 1)

1tbsp butter

15g ricotta cheese

2 eggs

25g spinach

1 slice of rye bread

TO MAKE

- Melt the butter in a saucepan.
- Add the ricotta and the eggs.
- Stir with a spatula until the mixture starts to set but is still slightly runny in places.
- Add the spinach and take the mixture off the heat.
- While the eggs are cooking, toast the rye bread.
- Give the eggs a final stir and serve.

Per portion Calories **357**/ Protein **18g** / Fat **17g** / Carbs **24g**

THE BENEFITS

RICOTTA CHEESE
provides whey protein, which builds muscle.

RYE BREAD
provides manganese, which boosts metabolism.

SPINACH
provides octacosanol, which increases muscle strength.

HAM HOCK OMELETTE

Get a flying start on your day's protein intake and beat the mid-morning slump with this meaty breakfast creation

INGREDIENTS

(SERVES 2)

4 eggs
1tsp butter
50g ham hock, shredded
2 handfuls of
cooked spinach
½ ball of mozzarella,
torn into chunks
Small handful of
pumpkin seeds
½ chilli, diced

TO MAKE

- Whisk the eggs in a bowl.
- Heat the butter in a pan over a medium heat.
- Sauté the spinach for two minutes.
- Add the remaining ingredients to the eggs and stir.
- Add the egg mixture to the pan and stir it in with the spinach.
- Reduce the temperature to a low heat for five to six minutes until the omelette is cooked through.

Per portion Calories **831** / Protein **104g** / Fat **52g** / Carbs **21g**

THE BENEFITS

HAM HOCK
provides protein, which
builds muscle.

SPINACH
provides iron, which supplies
your muscles with oxygen.

MOZZARELLA
provides attention-
enhancing phosphorous.

EGGS BENEDICT

Convert this hangover-dismissing classic into a morning feast to fuel
your body and brain by serving it with coconut hollandaise sauce

INGREDIENTS

(SERVES 1)

2 whole eggs
2 egg yolks
1tbsp lemon juice
3tbsp coconut oil
½tsp salt
Pinch of paprika
1 muffin, sliced (optional)
50g ham

TO MAKE

- Fill a blender with boiling water.
- Cover with the lid and let it sit for ten minutes, then dry the blender, add the egg yolks and lemon juice and blend.
- In a pan, heat the coconut oil on a low heat. With the blender on low, pour in the hot coconut oil in a steady stream.
- Season with salt and paprika, then pulse a few times to combine.
- Bring a pan of water to a boil, then crack the eggs into it.
- Keep them at a low temperature for four minutes, then remove with a slotted spoon and dry on a sheet of kitchen roll.
- Toast the muffin and top with the ham, egg and hollandaise.
- If you want something a bit different, replace the ham with 60g spinach (cook in a pan with a little water for a few minutes) for eggs florentine, or 50g smoked salmon for eggs royale.

Per portion Calories **905** / Protein **36g** / Fat **74g** / Carbs **31g**

THE BENEFITS

COCONUT OIL
provides medium-chain fatty
acids, which boost energy.

HAM
provides magnesium, which
strengthens muscles.

LEMON JUICE
provides flavanols, which
protect against cancer.

EGG SALAD BAGEL

White bagels provide high-GI carbohydrate, which enters your bloodstream fast and drives the protein from the egg into your muscles, helping you to get more from your morning workout

INGREDIENTS
(SERVES 1)

1 white bagel, sliced
3tbsp low-fat mayonnaise
1tbsp Dijon mustard
1 boiled egg, sliced
1 tomato, sliced
1tbsp watercress
Black pepper to taste

TO MAKE
- Toast both halves of the bagel under a medium grill.
- Meanwhile, mix the mayonnaise with the mustard.
- Layer the mustard mayo, egg, tomato and watercress between the two halves of the bagel.

Per portion Calories **403** / Protein **13g** / Fat **24g** / Carbs **43g**

THE BENEFITS

EGG
provides amino acids,
which repair muscle tissue.

WATERCRESS
provides iron, which
increases energy levels.

TOMATO
provides lycopene,
which helps to
strengthen bones.

CHEAT DAY OAT PANCAKES

This indulgent yet nutritious pancake recipe swaps flour for porridge oats to help kick-start your day and avoid the dreaded mid-morning energy slump

INGREDIENTS

(SERVES 1)

3 egg whites

40g oats

½tsp baking powder

30g caster sugar

1tbsp Greek yogurt

1tsp honey

30g crushed hazelnuts

½ banana, sliced

Pinch of cinnamon

20g dark chocolate (ideally 80% cocoa)

TO MAKE

- Blend the egg whites, oats, baking powder and caster sugar.
- Heat a little butter in a pan and add as much of the egg mix as you want to form a pancake.
- Cook until it bubbles, then flip and cook for a further three minutes.
- Repeat as required.
- Serve the pancakes with the yogurt, honey, hazelnuts, banana and a pinch of cinnamon. Melt the chocolate on top to finish.

Per portion Calories **610** / Protein **25g** / Fat **17g** / Carbs **83g**

THE BENEFITS

DARK CHOCOLATE
provides tryptophan, which suppresses food cravings.

GREEK YOGURT
provides low-GI carbs, which maintain energy and steady blood sugar levels.

HAZELNUTS
provide protein, which builds muscle.

BACON PANCAKES WITH MAPLE SYRUP

Recover from your morning workout and boost testosterone with this indulgent American-style brunch recipe, which includes high levels of blood-sugar stabilising manganese

INGREDIENTS

(SERVES 2)

230g wholemeal flour
½tsp salt
50g caster sugar
½tsp bicarbonate of soda
1tbsp baking powder
530ml semi-skimmed milk
2 free-range eggs
100ml rapeseed oil
6 rashers of lean
smoked back bacon
4tbsp maple syrup

TO MAKE

- Whisk the flour, salt, sugar, bicarbonate of soda, baking powder, milk and eggs together to make a batter. Pour it through a fine sieve to remove any lumps.
- Heat a little rapeseed oil in a non-stick frying pan over a medium heat.
- Spoon the batter into the centre of the pan until it's approximately 1cm high and 5cm wide.
- Fry the pancake until golden brown on one side, then flip it and cook on the other side.
- Once both sides are golden brown, remove from the frying pan and place on a plate.
- Repeat the process to make three more pancakes.
- While the pancakes are cooking, place the bacon rashers under a hot grill. Cook until golden on both sides.
- Place the bacon on the pancakes and drizzle the maple syrup over the top.

Per portion Calories **1,053** / Protein **38g** / Fat **41g** / Carbs **136g**

THE BENEFITS

BACON
provides protein,
which fills you up.

MILK
provides calcium,
which strengthens bone.

MAPLE SYRUP
provides manganese,
which helps to metabolise
fats and carbs.

MUSHROOM MUFFINS

Bin the refined carbs and get on track for a flat stomach with this ingenious recipe that swaps a blood-sugar spiking muffin for a fibrous portobello mushroom

INGREDIENTS

(SERVES 2)

3 portobello mushrooms
3tbsp rapeseed oil
3 eggs
3 rashers of bacon
Salt and pepper to taste

TO MAKE

- Brush the mushrooms with 1tbsp rapeseed oil and season them with the salt and pepper.
- Bake the mushrooms in an oven at 160°C/gas mark 3 for ten minutes.
- Fry the eggs over a medium heat in another 1tbsp oil for two to four minutes.
- Cook the bacon in the remaining oil for six minutes until crisp, turning halfway through.
- Layer the bacon and egg on top of the mushrooms, and serve.

Per portion Calories **873** / Protein **36g** / Fat **72g** / Carbs **15g**

THE BENEFITS

MUSHROOM
provides potassium, which improves energy levels.

BACON
provides vitamin B12, which is important for cardiovascular health.

EGG
provides vitamin D, which boosts immunity.

GRILLED KIPPERS

Feed your mind and your body with this British breakfast, which provides high levels of DHA – an essential brain-boosting fatty acid that's most effective in the morning

INGREDIENTS

(SERVES 1)

2 kippers
20g butter
1 lemon, halved

TO MAKE

- Put the kippers on an oven tray with two large knobs of butter on top.
- Place in an oven preheated to 200°C/gas mark 6 for about ten minutes until piping hot throughout.
- Serve with half a lemon.

Per portion Calories **364** / Protein **25g** / Fat **29g** / Carbs **0g**

THE BENEFITS

KIPPERS
provide vitamin D, which strengthens bones.

BUTTER
provides vitamin A, which boosts the immune system.

LEMON
provides vitamin C, which improves brain health.

KEDGEREE

Transform leftovers into a muscle-building feast with this healthy take on a classic Indian dish

INGREDIENTS

(SERVES 1)

45g basmati rice

3 cloves garlic, chopped

1 onion, chopped

1tbsp coconut oil

200g peas

300g smoked haddock

4 bay leaves

2 eggs

½tsp turmeric

2tsp curry powder

TO MAKE

- Cook the rice according to packaging instructions.
- In a separate pan, fry the garlic and onions in the coconut oil over a low heat until soft, then add the peas.
- Meanwhile, poach the haddock in water with the bay leaves until soft (this should take 15 minutes). Drain and flake into a bowl.
- At the same time, hard-boil or poach the eggs.
- Add the spices, rice and flaked fish to the onion mixture and combine well.
- Serve topped with the eggs.

Per portion Calories **920** / Protein **100g** / Fat **27g** / Carbs **61g**

THE BENEFITS

HADDOCK
provides vitamin B6, which helps the body metabolise carbohydrates.

BASMATI RICE
provides fibre, which fills you up.

PEAS
provide folate, which improves focus.

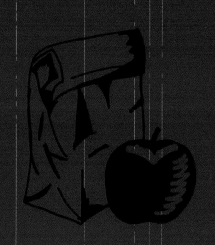

LUNCH

Whether you're refuelling after a morning workout, getting ready for an evening gym session or just looking for a simple, healthy midday meal, these lunch menus have you covered

CHICKEN BURGERS

These burgers provide plenty of muscle-building protein with far fewer calories than the usual beef variety, and they're perfect for a packed lunch

INGREDIENTS

(MAKES 3)

2 chicken breast fillets, cut into chunks
1 small onion, finely chopped
1tbsp olive oil
½ red pepper, chopped
½ green pepper, chopped
2tsp cinnamon
30g clear honey
Salt and pepper to taste

TO MAKE

- Warm half the oil in a frying pan over a medium heat. Add the onion and fry for five minutes, until softened.
- Meanwhile, place the chicken in a food processor and blend to a paste.
- Transfer the paste to a mixing bowl. Add the peppers, 1tsp of the cinnamon and half the honey, and mix it all together.
- Reduce the heat under the frying pan to low, add the rest of the honey and cinnamon to the onions and mix together.
- Cook for 15 minutes, resisting the temptation to stir too often.
- Remove from the heat and stir into the burger mixture.
- Divide the chicken mixture into three equal amounts. Use your hands to form these into burgers.
- Add the rest of the oil to the pan and turn up the heat to medium.
- Cook your burgers for a minute on each side to seal them, then reduce the heat to low and cook for ten minutes or so, flipping occasionally, until piping hot throughout.
- Eat one immediately, and keep the others for your lunchbox.

Per portion Calories **237** / Protein **28g** / Fat **8g** / Carbs **15g**

THE BENEFITS

CHICKEN
provides vitamin B3, which helps to prevent fat storage.

HONEY
provides iron, which boosts metabolism.

CINNAMON
provides antioxidants, which help to regulate blood sugar.

PARSNIP FRIED RICE

Skip the takeaway and feast on fried rice that *fights* fat
– with a little help from a roast dinner staple

INGREDIENTS

(SERVES 2)

2 large parsnips, peeled
and cut into chunks
1½tbsp rapeseed oil
1 onion, peeled and chopped
2 garlic cloves, crushed
1tsp peeled, grated ginger
1 courgette, cubed
100g chestnut
mushrooms, sliced
200g chicken breast,
cooked and shredded
2tbsp fresh coriander,
roughly chopped
Salt and pepper to taste

TO MAKE

- Blend the parsnips in a food processor until they reach a rice-like consistency. Put them in a bowl and set to one side.
- Heat the rapeseed oil in a large saucepan over a medium heat and add the onion, garlic, ginger and courgette. Cook for three to four minutes.
- Add the mushrooms and cook for a further five minutes.
- Stir in the parsnip rice and cook for another minute.
- Add the chicken and cook for an additional two to three minutes. Season with salt and pepper, add the coriander and serve.

Per portion Calories **823** / Protein **72g** / Fat **29g** / Carbs **74g**

THE BENEFITS

CHICKEN
provides protein, which
builds muscle.

PARSNIP
provides manganese,
which soothes muscle.

MUSHROOMS
provide fibre,
which fills you up.

SESAME CHICKEN SALAD WITH MANDARIN

The Paleo diet-inspired salad contains only ingredients that our caveman ancestors would have eaten, and no processed foods or refined sugars

INGREDIENTS

(SERVES 2)

2 chicken breasts
4tbsp sesame oil
1 garlic clove, crushed
1 red chilli, seeded and
finely chopped
2tsp fresh ginger, grated
150g baby spinach
Handful of basil and
coriander leaves
½ red onion, chopped
5 almonds, chopped
1tsp sesame seeds
1 mandarin, divided
into segments

TO MAKE

- Mix the sesame oil, garlic, chilli and ginger in a bowl.
- Slash the chicken in several places and marinade in the sesame oil mixture for four hours.
- Add the baby spinach leaves to a bowl with the herbs, onion, almonds and sesame seeds.
- Baste the chicken with the marinade mix and grill for 20 minutes, or until the juices run clear.
- Cut the chicken into strips and add to the salad.
- Dress with the remainder of the sesame oil and mandarin.

Per portion Calories **428** / Protein **19g** / Fat **14g** / Carbs **15g**

THE BENEFITS

RED ONION
provides sulphur, which strengthens the body's connective tissue.

MANDARIN
provides vitamin C, which boosts immunity.

ALMONDS
provide manganese, which soothes muscles.

SCOTCH EGGS

A protein-packed double whammy of egg and sausagemeat makes this classic snack an ideal post-gym treat – provided you avoid the perils of the supermarket variety and make it yourself

INGREDIENTS

(MAKES 4)

5 large free-range eggs
275g Cumberland sausagemeat
Freshly ground black pepper
125g plain flour
125g dried wholemeal breadcrumbs
2tbsp rapeseed oil

TO MAKE

- Boil four eggs in a pan of water over a medium heat for six minutes.
- Remove the eggs from the pan and place them in a bowl of ice water for five minutes. Remove the eggs from the water and and carefully peel them.
- Divide the sausagemeat into four balls and flatten them using the palm of your hand.
- Place an egg on each of the sausagemeat patties and carefully wrap it up, ensuring all of each egg is fully covered and sealed.
- Beat the fifth egg and season the flour with the pepper.
- Dip each sausagemeat-coated egg in the flour, then the beaten egg and finally the breadcrumbs. Ensure each egg is fully covered at every stage.
- Heat the rapeseed oil in a pan over a medium heat, then shallow-fry the scotch eggs for four minutes, turning frequently with a slotted spoon.
- Carefully remove the eggs from the pan and place on kitchen roll to remove any excess oil.

Per portion Calories **576** / Protein **24g** / Fat **27g** / Carbs **35g**

THE BENEFITS

EGG
provides iron, which boosts energy.

PORK
provides vitamin B1, which supports your nervous system.

RAPESEED OIL
provides vitamin E, which protects against heart disease.

POUTINE

This chips, cheese and gravy dish from Canada offers valuable nutrients to help you get ripped despite being pretty decadent. Go on, treat yourself

INGREDIENTS

(SERVES 2)

300g sweet potatoes, peeled and cut into wedges
2tsp butter
1 clove garlic, crushed
100ml gravy (ready-made)
4 rashers of bacon
50g cheddar cheese, grated
2tbsp rapeseed oil
Salt and pepper to taste

TO MAKE

- Mix together the butter and garlic and brush it over the sweet potato. Season with salt and pepper.
- Place the wedges on a baking tray and cook at 180°C/gas mark 4 for 20 minutes, turning regularly so they cook evenly.
- Make the gravy according to packaging instructions.
- Remove the baking tray from the oven, pour the gravy into it, grate the cheddar over the top and stir it in.
- Return to the oven for 20 minutes, or until the cheese is crunchy.
- Heat the oil in a pan over a medium heat and cook the bacon for five minutes until crisp, turning halfway through. Serve the chips with the bacon on top.

Per portion Calories **656** / Protein **33g** / Fat **29g** / Carbs **44g**

THE BENEFITS

SWEET POTATO
provides vitamin A, which boosts immunity.

BACON
provides phosphorous, which maintains efficient kidney function.

CHEDDAR CHEESE
provides conjugated linoleic acid, which helps to reduce body fat.

MINESTRONE SOUP

A hearty Italian broth that's packed with muscle-building nutrients, this enhanced minestrone also features plenty of muscle-building ham

INGREDIENTS

(SERVES 4)

50ml rapeseed oil
2 carrots, peeled and diced
1 fennel bulb, diced
1 onion, diced
2 sticks of celery, diced
2 garlic cloves, crushed
2 bay leaves
300g cherry tomatoes, halved
300g cooked ham, cut into strips
1 litre chicken stock
300ml tomato juice
100g wholemeal spaghetti
Salt and pepper

TO MAKE

- Heat the oil in a large saucepan over a medium heat.
- Add the carrots, fennel, onion, celery, garlic and bay leaves, and cook for five to seven minutes.
- Add the cherry tomatoes, cover and cook for ten minutes.
- Add the ham and cook until the tomatoes are soft, then add the chicken stock and tomato juice.
- Bring to the boil, reduce the heat and simmer for five minutes.
- Cook the spaghetti according to packaging instructions, then cut into 2cm lengths and add to the broth.
- Bring it back to the boil, season with salt and pepper and serve.

Per portion Calories **321** / Protein **17g** / Fat **15g** / Carbs **28g**

THE BENEFITS

HAM
provides vitamin B1, which promotes energy production.

CELERY
provides potassium, which improves kidney health.

WHOLEMEAL SPAGHETTI
provides fibre, which aids digestion.

CRAB WITH PARSNIP CHIPS

Cracking open a crustacean will provide maximum muscle-building protein for minimal calories – ideal if you want to carve a lean set of abs without losing existing muscle mass

INGREDIENTS

(SERVES 1)

225g crabmeat, picked
and cleaned
1tbsp curly parsley,
finely chopped
3tbsp natural yogurt
2 pinches of
cayenne pepper
Juice of 1 pink grapefruit
2 parsnips, peeled and
sliced into thin chips
3tbsp rapeseed oil
Salt to taste

TO MAKE

- Mix the crabmeat, parsley, yogurt and cayenne pepper in a bowl.
- Add the grapefruit juice to taste, mix thoroughly and place in the fridge.
- Heat the oil in a pan and cook the parsnips over a medium heat for 15 minutes, tossing the pan every two minutes.
- Season the chips with salt and serve them with the crab mixture.

Per portion Calories **933** / Protein **54g** / Fat **47g** / Carbs **73g**

THE BENEFITS

CRABMEAT
provides copper, which
strengthens bones.

NATURAL YOGURT
provides calcium, which
strengthens bones.

PARSNIP
provides fibre, which
aids digestion.

SPICY FISH STEW

Kick your metabolism into action with DHA-stuffed salmon
and a hit of hot spices with this fat-burning broth

INGREDIENTS

(SERVES 3)

100g monkfish
4 scallops
100g salmon
Handful of mussels
1tbsp olive oil
4 new potatoes, halved
1 red onion, chopped
1 red pepper, chopped
3 cloves of garlic, crushed
1 chilli, diced
1tbsp ginger, chopped
400g can
chopped tomatoes
200ml fish stock
1tbsp saffron
Pinch of cumin
Pinch of paprika
1tsp lemon juice
1tsp chopped coriander

TO MAKE

- Heat the olive oil in a deep pan and cook the potatoes for four minutes on a medium heat.
- Add the onion, pepper, garlic, chilli and ginger and sauté for two minutes.
- Add the tomatoes and cook on a low heat for five minutes.
- Add the fish stock and all the spices and cook for ten minutes.
- Add all the seafood and cook for eight minutes.
- Serve and garnish with the lemon juice and coriander.

Per portion Calories **559** / Protein **48g** / Fat **13g** / Carbs **63g**

THE BENEFITS

SALMON
provides omega 3, which
improves joint health.

NEW POTATO
provides vitamin C, which
boosts immunity.

TOMATO
provides biotin, which
balances blood sugar.

SALMON FILLET WITH PESTO

After a punishing workout, few foods can soothe your aching muscles like salmon, which is rich in muscle-repairing protein and inflammation-reducing omega 3 fatty acids

INGREDIENTS
(SERVES 1)

1 large salmon fillet
1tbsp pesto
6 new potatoes
Handful of broccoli
1tbsp lemon juice

TO MAKE
- Preheat the oven to 180°C/gas mark 4.
- Place the salmon on a baking tray and spread the pesto over the top. Cook in the oven for ten to 15 minutes until the pesto forms a crust and the salmon is cooked through.
- Boil the new potatoes in a pan for ten to 12 minutes until soft. At the same time, steam the broccoli for five minutes.
- Pour the lemon juice over the salmon and serve.

Per portion Calories **413** / Protein **21g** / Fat **26g** / Carbs **30g**

THE BENEFITS

PESTO
provides protein, which builds muscle.

LEMON JUICE
provides folate, which improves brain health.

POTATO
provides starch, which helps your body to burn calories.

RATATOUILLE

A quick and super-simple version of the classic French stew recipe,
packed with filling, nutrient-rich vegetables

INGREDIENTS
(SERVES 2)

1 red pepper, diced
1 yellow pepper, diced
2 courgettes, diced
1 aubergine, diced
1 red onion, diced
2 cloves of garlic, minced
2tbsp olive oil
Sprigs of thyme
Salt and pepper

TO MAKE

- Heat the oil in a pan and sauté all the vegetables with the thyme and garlic for ten minutes or until soft.
- Drain in a colander to remove any excess liquid.
- Eat with fish, grilled chicken or simply on sourdough toast as a snack.

Per portion Calories **319** / Protein **10g** / Fat **14g** / Carbs **44g**

THE BENEFITS

YELLOW PEPPER
provides vitamin C, which
boosts immunity.

COURGETTE
provides manganese,
which improves blood
sugar control.

AUBERGINE
provides fibre, which
aids digestion.

BROCCOLI AND STILTON SOUP

This easy-to-make soup provides plenty of energy-boosting chromium
– just throw all the cooked ingredients in a blender and blitz

INGREDIENTS
(SERVES 2)

250g broccoli, cut
into florets
1tbsp olive oil
1 onion, diced
1 garlic clove, crushed
Handful of spinach
150ml vegetable stock
2tbsp stilton, crumbled
1tbsp toasted almonds
Salt and pepper to taste

TO MAKE

- Heat the oil in a pan over a medium heat.
- Add the onion and garlic and cook until softened.
- Add the broccoli, spinach and stock. Bring to the boil and cook for three to five minutes.
- Remove the mixture from the pan and blend until smooth.
- Season and serve with the crumbled stilton and toasted almonds on top.

Per portion Calories **253** / Protein **11g** / Fat **19g** / Carbs **13g**

THE BENEFITS

BROCCOLI
provides vitamin K, which
strengthens bones.

STILTON
provides vitamin A, which
boosts immunity.

ONION
provides quercetin, which
soothes inflammation.

SPICY VEG AND NOODLE SOUP

Feast on veg with this immunity-boosting noodle dish to stay strong and healthy all year round

INGREDIENTS
(SERVES 1)

½ onion, chopped
1 clove of garlic, crushed
1cm ginger, grated
120ml water
1 vegetable stock cube
100ml coconut milk
Juice of 1 lime
1tsp fresh coriander leaves, chopped
1tsp turmeric
1tsp chilli powder
1tsp tamari or soy sauce
20g edamame beans
20g cooked kelp noodles
20g cooked rice noodles
20g leek, shredded
20g kale, shredded
1g pumpkin seeds
1g chia seeds

TO MAKE
- Heat a large, heavy pot over medium-high heat. Stir in the onion, garlic and ginger and sauté until the onion has softened.
- Pour in the water, stock cube, coconut milk and lime juice and stir in the coriander, turmeric, chilli powder and tamari.
- Bring to the boil and cook for ten minutes.
- Add the edamame and cook for four minutes.
- Add the noodles, leek and kale, reduce the heat to medium-low and cook until edamame are just off firm.
- Serve in a soup bowl garnished with pumpkin and chia seeds.

Per portion Calories **347** / Protein **8g** / Fat **26g** / Carbs **27g**

THE BENEFITS

LEEK
provides folate, which improves brain health.

KALE
provides vitamin E, which protects against heart disease.

EDAMAME BEANS
provide fibre, which fills you up.

HUEVOS RANCHEROS

This vegetarian-friendly Mexican dish is packed with high-protein foods that will help repair and grow muscle tissue, including the potent bulk-building trio of eggs, cheese and kidney beans

INGREDIENTS
(SERVES 2)

2tbsp olive oil
1 onion, peeled
and finely sliced
1 garlic clove, peeled
and finely sliced
1 red pepper, deseeded
and finely sliced
1 fresh red chilli, deseeded
and finely sliced
1 large dried chilli
2 fresh bay leaves
400g can chopped
tomatoes
400g can kidney beans
2 large tomatoes, sliced
4 large eggs
50g cheddar cheese, grated
2 wholemeal tortillas
Salt and pepper to taste

TO MAKE
- Heat the olive oil in a large frying pan over a medium heat.
- Add the onion, garlic, pepper, fresh and dried chillies, bay leaves and salt and pepper. Cook for 15 minutes until soft, stirring regularly.
- Pour in the canned tomatoes and kidney beans, using a spoon to break them up a bit. Bring to the boil, then lower the heat and cook for a further five minutes so the sauce starts to reduce.
- Lay the tomato slices over the top of the mixture, leaving four small gaps, and crack the eggs into the gaps so they poach in the juices.
- Cover with a lid or foil and let the eggs cook for four to five minutes.
- Sprinkle the grated cheese on top and serve with the warm tortillas.

Per portion Calories **798** / Protein **39g** / Fat **35g** / Carbs **91g**

THE BENEFITS

TOMATO
provides vitamin K,
which helps maintain
normal blood function.

EGG
provides selenium, which
enables cells to combat
exercise-related damage.

CHEDDAR CHEESE
provides calcium, which
strengthens bones.

DINNER

Mastering these muscle-building, fat-burning mains
– all of which are quick and easy to prepare – will provide you
with plenty of healthy options for your evening meal

SPICY CHICKEN BURGER WITH SWEET POTATO RÖSTI

On cheat day if you're tempted by a dirty burger try this
zingy, fat-burning stack of goodness instead

INGREDIENTS

(SERVES 1)

1 chicken breast, butterflied

1 egg, beaten

1tbsp wholemeal flour

2 handfuls of breadcrumbs

1tsp chilli flakes

50ml rapeseed oil

½ sweet potato, peeled
and grated

1tbsp cornflour

Salt and pepper

25g unsalted butter

1 wholemeal bun

1tsp tomato ketchup

1 slice of cheddar cheese

1 slice of tomato

Handful of cooked kale

TO MAKE

- Dust the chicken with the flour, then dip in the egg.
- Mix the breadcrumbs and chilli flakes in a shallow dish. Press the chicken into breadcrumb mix to coat it on both sides.
- Fry the chicken in the rapeseed oil over a medium heat for four minutes on each side until it's cooked through and the breadcrumbs are golden brown.
- To make the rösti, mix the grated potato and cornflour in a bowl and season. Heat the butter in a frying pan and add the potato mixture, pressing down to make an even surface.
- Fry for two minutes or until golden, then turn and fry for a further two minutes.
- Place in an oven heated to 190°/gas mark 5 and cook for five minutes.
- Cut the bun in half and spread the tomato ketchup on the inside of the top slice. Add the chicken, cheese, kale, tomato and rösti.

Per portion Calories **1,181** / Protein **114g** / Fat **63g** / Carbs **159g**

THE BENEFITS

CHICKEN
provides vitamin B6, which
helps break down carbs for
energy production.

SWEET POTATO
provides iron, which
combats fatigue.

TOMATO
provides phytonutrients
that boost heart health.

SWEET AND SOUR TURKEY

This rich, tangy turkey recipe uses ingredients that will
help you burn fat alongside your training

INGREDIENTS

(SERVES 2)

500g turkey breast,
cut into strips

2tbsp rapeseed oil

1 onion, sliced

2tbsp tomato purée

3tbsp malt vinegar

1tbsp Muscovado sugar

2tbsp dark soy sauce

225g can pineapple
chunks in natural juice

2 carrots, peeled and
thinly sliced

160g brown rice

TO MAKE

- Heat half the rapeseed oil in a pan over a medium heat.
- Add the onion and cook until browned. Add the purée, vinegar, sugar and soy sauce, and stir.
- Add the pineapple chunks and their juice, along with the carrots.
- Cook for four minutes, then set aside. Season the turkey with salt and pepper, then heat the remaining oil and fry the meat until cooked through.
- Return the sauce to the pan, stir thoroughly and cook for five minutes.
- Cook the rice according to packaging instructions, then serve with the sauce.

Per portion Calories **751** / Protein **61g** / Fat **31g** / Carbs **50g**

THE BENEFITS

TURKEY
provides protein,
which builds muscle and
keeps you feeling full.

ONION
provides chromium,
which helps to control
insulin response.

PINEAPPLE
provides manganese,
which helps to regulate
blood sugar levels.

PAN-SEARED PORK CHOPS

This recipe twins a classic bargain cut of meat with bone-strengthening, vitamin K-stuffed cabbage

INGREDIENTS

(SERVES 4)

4 bone-in pork chops
1tbsp chopped fresh thyme
2½tbsp olive oil
1tsp whole caraway seeds
1 small onion, thinly sliced
2 rashers of bacon, sliced
100ml white wine vinegar
½ medium green or
white cabbage, cored
and thinly sliced
1tbsp chopped fresh
flat-leaf parsley
125ml chicken stock
2tbsp wholegrain mustard
2tbsp hoisin sauce
1tbsp chopped fresh herbs
1tbsp chopped fresh chives
Salt and pepper to taste

TO MAKE

- Preheat the oven to 200°C/gas mark 6. Heat a heavy, ovenproof pan over medium-high heat.
- Season the chops on both sides with salt, pepper and thyme. Heat 2tbsp of the oil in the pan, and add the pork chops, making sure they're 2-3cm apart.
- Cook for two to three minutes until the underside is golden brown. Turn and sear for another minute. Transfer the pan to the oven and cook until the chops are cooked through but still slightly pink in the middle, which should take 12 to 15 minutes. Cover and keep warm.
- Meanwhile, in another pan, heat the remaining olive oil over a medium-high heat. Add the caraway seeds and onion and sauté for two minutes, stirring, until the onion starts to soften.
- Add the bacon and continue to cook for three to five minutes until the onion starts to brown. Add the vinegar, turn up the heat to high, and stir and scrape with a wooden spoon to deglaze the pan.
- Add the cabbage and cook for three to four minutes, stirring, until it is just heated through. Stir in the parsley. Cover and keep warm.
- Pour off all of the fat from the pan in which the pork chops were cooked. Return the pan to a medium-high heat and pour in the stock. With a wooden spoon, stir and scrape to deglaze the pan.
- Boil it briefly, stirring, until it has reduced slightly. Stir in the mustard, hoisin sauce and herbs, and season with salt and pepper if required.

Per portion Calories **921** / Protein **134g** / Fat **32g** / Carbs **15g**

THE BENEFITS

PORK
provides magnesium, which supports muscles.

CABBAGE
provides vitamin K, which strengthens bones.

MUSTARD
provides selenium, which improves sleep.

GUINNESS STEAK

Don't be fooled by the booze – this simple steak recipe offers potent cancer-fighting, free radical-crushing benefits

INGREDIENTS

(SERVES 2)

400g boneless rib-eye
steak, 4cm thick
250ml Guinness
100g finely chopped onion
100ml soy sauce
20ml maple syrup
1 sprig rosemary,
leaves chopped
1 sprig thyme,
leaves chopped
1tbsp garlic, finely chopped
1tsp Worcestershire sauce
Salt and pepper to taste

TO MAKE

- Combine the beer, onion, soy sauce, maple syrup, rosemary, thyme, garlic and Worcestershire sauce in a large sealable plastic bag. Add the steak. Seal the bag, shake and turn it, and refrigerate overnight.
- Take the meat out of the fridge and bag 20 minutes before cooking to bring it up to room temperature. Fire up the grill.
- Just before cooking, lightly season the meat with salt and black pepper.
- Don't use any oil on the meat or in the pan – if the grill is hot enough, the meat won't stick. Put the steak under the grill. Leave it for a minute and then turn.
- Carry on turning every minute until it's the way you like it.
- If the steak is really thick, turn more regularly to avoid burning – the marinade will make this more likely so keep an eye on it. If you're cooking more than one steak, make sure there's plenty of space between them.
- As a rough guide, though, cook it for three minutes on each side then rest it for ten minutes. The key thing is to take it off just before you think it's ready and leave it to rest.
- Cook the marinade to reduce it to a glaze. Drizzle over the steak and serve.

Per portion Calories **1,379** / Protein **89g** / Fat **88g** / Carbs **38g**

THE BENEFITS

BEEF STEAK
provides creatine,
which builds muscle.

MAPLE SYRUP
provides calcium, which
strengthens bones.

ONION
provides biotin, which is
crucial for skin health.

CHILLI BURGER AND WEDGES

If you only eat burgers at McDonald's, then you're missing out. Homemade burgers can be far healthier – not to mention tastier – and they're surprisingly straightforward to prepare

INGREDIENTS

(SERVES 1)

220g lean steak mice

2 sweet potatoes, peeled and cut into wedges

1tbsp olive oil

½ onion, diced

½ chilli, chopped

Pinch of black pepper

2 slices of tomato

1 slice of cheddar

A handful of baby spinach leaves

2 slices of red onion

1 wholemeal burger bun

TO MAKE

- Preheat the oven to 200°C/gas mark 6.
- Toss the potato wedges in olive oil and roast them in the oven for 20 minutes, turning them halfway through.
- Mix the mince, onion, chilli and black pepper and shape it into a burger.
- Grill the burger until cooked to your preference, turning it halfway through.
- Place the spinach and red onion on the bottom half of the bun. Put the burger on top, followed by the cheese, tomato and the top of the bun. Serve with the potato wedges.

Per portion Calories **846** / Protein **49g** / Fat **56g** / Carbs **85g**

THE BENEFITS

STEAK MINCE
provides zinc, which boosts immunity.

CHILLI
provides capsaicin, which boosts metabolism.

SWEET POTATO
provides betacarotene, which improves heart health.

T-BONE STEAK

This mighty meat is packed with muscle-building protein and is quick and easy to prepare

INGREDIENTS

(SERVES 1)

900g T-bone steak
1tbsp rapeseed oil
1tbsp butter
1tsp wholegrain mustard
Salt and pepper to taste

TO MAKE

- Make sure the steak is at room temperature before cooking.
- Heat a frying pan until it begins to smoke. Brush the steak with the rapeseed oil (1tbsp on each side) and rub with salt and pepper.
- Cook the steak in the pan for seven minutes on each side, basting regularly with the butter and mustard.
- Take the pan off the heat. Leave the steak to rest for five minutes before serving.

Per portion Calories **1,096** / Protein **119g** / Fat **65g** / Carbs **1g**

THE BENEFITS

BEEF STEAK
provides B12, which keeps your brain healthy.

MUSTARD
provides selenium, which improves sleep.

BUTTER
provides conjugated linoleic acid, which is used for energy production.

SEAFOOD CHOWDER

This satisfying soup is one of the most effective muscle-builders you can eat, featuring six different types of seafood which all offer excellent protein-to-calorie ratios

INGREDIENTS

(SERVES 2)

150g pollock, cut into chunks
150g cod, cut into chunks
150g haddock, cut into chunks
150g raw tiger prawns
50g mussels
50g clams
100ml rapeseed oil
1 onion, diced
3 garlic cloves, crushed
1 fennel bulb, diced
1tsp smoked paprika
400g can chopped tomatoes
750ml chicken stock
2tbsp curly parsley, finely chopped
Salt and pepper to taste

TO MAKE

● Heat the oil in a large thick-bottomed saucepan.
● Add the onion, garlic and fennel to the pan and cook gently until the onion softens, then stir in the smoked paprika.
● Add the tomatoes and stock. Bring to the boil, then simmer gently for ten minutes.
● Reduce the heat and add the fish and shellfish to the pan. Simmer for four minutes or until the clams and mussels are open and the fish is almost cooked through, then add the prawns and cook until they turn pink.
● Season with salt and pepper, sprinkle the parsley on top and serve.

Per portion Calories **534** / Protein **41g** / Fat **28g** / Carbs **17g**

THE BENEFITS

HADDOCK
provides protein, which builds muscle.

RAPESEED OIL
provides omega 3 fatty acids, which soothe inflammation.

PARSLEY
provides folic acid, which improves cardiovascular health.

MOULES MARINIÈRE

This upgraded mussels recipe swaps calorific double cream for vitamin B12-rich natural yogurt to give you an extras energy boost

INGREDIENTS

(SERVES 1)

1.5kg mussels in shells, cleaned and beards removed
1 bay leaf
100ml dry white wine
4 shallots, peeled and sliced
20g unsalted butter
2tbsp natural yogurt
25g curly parsley, roughly chopped

CLEANING THE MUSSELS

- Wash the mussels in a pot under cold running water. If any of the mussels float, discard them.
- Press the shells of any open mussels together with your fingers. If they don't close, discard them.
- Scrape off any barnacles with a sharp knife and pull out the beards.

TO MAKE

- Heat the butter in a large pan over a medium heat. Add the shallots and bay leaf, and soften for one minute.
- Add the mussels and white wine, cover the pan tightly with a lid and cook for four to five minutes until the mussels have all opened.
- Stir in the natural yogurt and chopped parsley, and serve.

Per portion Calories **751** / Protein **65g** / Fat **27g** / Carbs **43g**

THE BENEFITS

MUSSELS
provide manganese, which strengthens bones.

NATURAL YOGURT
provides protein, which builds muscle.

SHALLOT
provides quercetin, which soothes inflammation.

THAI PRAWN CURRY

Curry may be Britain's favourite takeaway, but that shouldn't stop you from making your own at home, especially when it can be this healthy, tasty and easy to cook

INGREDIENTS

(SERVES 2)

15 fresh prawns
1tbsp olive oil
2 small onions, chopped
2 carrots, chopped
2 fresh tomatoes, chopped
1 garlic clove, crushed
1 small piece of ginger, peeled and sliced
½tsp cayenne pepper
2 green chillies, sliced
1tbsp medium curry powder
½tsp turmeric
3tbsp oyster sauce
1 litre vegetable stock
100ml coconut milk
250g brown rice
½ lemongrass stick
1-2 medium green peppers, chopped
6-7 fresh coriander leaves, chopped

TO MAKE

- Heat the olive oil in a pan, add the onions and carrots and cook gently for five minutes.
- Add the tomatoes, garlic, ginger, cayenne pepper, green chillies, curry powder, turmeric, oyster sauce, stock and coconut milk.
- Simmer for 12-15 minutes to allow the sauce to thicken.
- Meanwhile, cook the rice according to packaging instructions.
- Drain the rice and use the water with added lemongrass to blanch the prawns for three to four minutes.
- Add the prawns, green peppers and coriander to the sauce and serve.

Per portion Calories **623** / Protein **23g** / Fat **14g** / Carbs **115g**

THE BENEFITS

PRAWN
provides protein, which builds muscle.

CARROT
provides betacarotene, which strengthens bones.

COCONUT
provides lauric acid, which promotes good cardiovascular health.

PRAWN PAD THAI

This simple seafood-packed noodle dish is a tasty and nutritious way to get the carbs you need before a big race

INGREDIENTS

(SERVES 2)

250g udon noodles
10 small broccoli florets
Small handful of green beans
2tsp rapeseed oil
3 cloves garlic, chopped
2 red chillies, deseeded and chopped
2 shallots, finely chopped
20 large tiger prawns, cleaned and de-shelled
2 egg whites
1tbsp sesame oil
3tbsp fish sauce
1tbsp soy sauce
1tbsp rice wine vinegar
1tbsp agave syrup
3 spring onions, chopped
2tbsp chopped peanuts
Handful of fresh coriander
1tbsp lime juice

TO MAKE

- Boil the noodles for three minutes, then drain, rinse and set aside.
- Blanch the broccoli and green beans in boiling water for one to two minutes. Drain, plunge into cold water and set aside.
- Heat a wok and add 1tsp rapeseed oil, plus the garlic, chilli and shallots. Cook over a medium heat for one minute. Add the prawns and cook for a further two minutes until pinkish. Remove and set aside.
- Add the remaining rapeseed oil and the egg whites. Cook gently, breaking them up as you do so, then put to one side with the prawn mix.
- To the empty pan add the sesame oil, fish sauce, soy sauce, rice wine vinegar and agave syrup and cook for two minutes.
- Turn the up the heat and return the prawns and egg to the wok with the spring onions, blanched veg and noodles.
- Remove from the heat and serve immediately garnished with the peanuts, coriander and lime juice.

Per portion Calories **923** / Protein **49g** / Fat **21g** / Carbs **148g**

THE BENEFITS

BROCCOLI
provides chromium, which regulates blood sugar levels.

EGG WHITE
provides protein, which builds muscle.

PEANUT
provides monounsaturated fats, which improve heart health.

COURGETTE AND TOMATO GRATIN

This hearty dish is packed with immunity-boosting antioxidants
to help you stay on top of your game

INGREDIENTS

(SERVES 2)

400g courgettes, sliced lengthways
5tbsp olive oil
1 clove of garlic, crushed
2tbsp grated parmesan cheese
1tbsp polenta
2tbsp chopped mixed fresh herbs (basil, chives, oregano, parsley)
400g ripe beef tomatoes, cored and sliced
Salt and pepper to taste

TO MAKE

- Preheat the oven to 200°C/gas mark 4.
- Toss the courgettes with 3tbsp of the oil.
- Heat a grill or griddle pan until hot, and grill the courgette slices on both sides until tender.
- Put the garlic, cheese, polenta and herbs into a bowl and mix together.
- Oil an ovenproof dish and start layering the veg, starting with a layer of courgettes, then a layer of tomatoes and a sprinkling of the cheesy herb mix. Season each layer and drizzle with the remaining olive oil.
- Finish with a layer of the cheesy herb mix and bake in the oven for about 20 minutes, until golden on top.

Per portion Calories **413** / Protein **8g** / Fat **37g** / Carbs **20g**

THE BENEFITS

COURGETTE
provides copper, which strengthens bones.

TOMATO
provides potassium, which helps to maintain healthy blood pressure.

PARMESAN
provides phosphorous, which boosts energy levels.

RED BEAN STEW

This vegan-friendly recipe feeds your body with plant protein for new muscle growth, along with healthy fats and slow-release carbohydrates to fuel your workouts and boost recovery

INGREDIENTS

(SERVES 2)

440g red kidney beans
250g pinto beans
250g chickpeas
100g soya beans
1 red onion, chopped
6 garlic cloves,
finely chopped
2tbsp rapeseed oil
2 red pepper, diced
3 stalks of celery, diced
2tsp tomato purée
2tsp Worcestershire sauce
1tsp Tabasco sauce
1 bay leaf
400g can chopped
tomatoes
1 vegetable stock cube
300ml water
Freshly ground
black pepper

TO MAKE

- In a deep pot over a medium heat, fry the onion and garlic in the rapeseed oil for five minutes.
- Add the peppers and celery and cook for a further two minutes.
- Add the tomato purée, Worcestershire sauce and Tabasco, and cook for another minute.
- Add the bay leaf, chopped tomato, stock cube and water and cook for five minutes.
- Add the beans and chickpeas, reduce the heat, cover and simmer for 20 minutes. Season with black pepper and serve.

Per portion Calories **419** / Protein **23g** / Fat **9g** / Carbs **61g**

THE BENEFITS

KIDNEY BEANS
provide folate, which
improves circulation.

RED PEPPER
provides vitamin A,
which boosts immunity.

CELERY
provides vitamin K, which
strengthens bones.

CHICKPEA BALTI

You don't always need to eat meat to build muscle – this tasty vegetarian curry offers plenty of nutrients to help you train harder, recover faster and, most importantly, pack on lean muscle

INGREDIENTS

(SERVES 2)

Handful of
cauliflower florets
1 onion, cut into chunks
1 sweet potato, chopped
into 3cm cubes
1 courgette, sliced
1 red pepper, chopped
into 3cm chunks
Handful of frozen peas
200g can chickpeas

FOR THE SAUCE

1 large onion, chopped
2.5cm ginger, peeled
and chopped
1 garlic clove, crushed
4tsp curry paste
400g can chopped
tomatoes
Large handful of coriander,
finely chopped

TO MAKE

- For the sauce, sweat the onion, ginger and garlic in a large heavy pan over a medium heat for a few minutes. Add the curry paste, chopped tomatoes and coriander, and simmer for a further ten minutes.
- Meanwhile, steam the cauliflower, onion, sweet potato, courgette and pepper until soft.
- Tip the steamed vegetables into the pan with the sauce. Add the peas and chickpeas and mix.
- Cook gently for five minutes and serve.

Per portion Calories **816** / Protein **30g** / Fat **15g** / Carbs **140g**

THE BENEFITS

CHICKPEAS
provide fibre, which
fills you up.

COURGETTE
provides folate, which helps
to maintain a healthy
nervous system.

RED PEPPER
provides vitamin C, which
improves recovery.

LIGHT MEALS

Eating healthy can be tricky if you're short on time.
That's why all the recipes in this chapter have been
designed to take ten minutes or less

CHICKEN CAESAR SALAD

This upgraded classic features bonus servings of bacon plus a healthy dressing consisting of protein-rich yogurt, anchovy and parmesan to help you pack on lean muscle

INGREDIENTS

(SERVES 1)

1 chicken breast,
grilled and sliced
2 rashers of bacon,
grilled and chopped
½ cos lettuce,
roughly chopped
2 slices of wholemeal bread,
toasted and broken into
crouton-size pieces

FOR THE DRESSING
4tbsp natural yogurt
1 anchovy, finely chopped
1tbsp parmesan,
finely grated
Salt and pepper

TO MAKE

- Mix the dressing ingredients together.
- Mix all the remaining ingredients, garnish with the dressing and serve.

Per portion Calories **765** / Protein **80g** / Fat **31g** / Carbs **38g**

THE BENEFITS

BACON
provides vitamin B3,
which helps to convert
macronutrients into energy.

WHOLEMEAL BREAD
provides fibre, which
makes you feel full.

PARMESAN
provides calcium, which
strengthens bones.

CHICKEN AND MOZZARELLA BAGEL

This Caprese bagel recipe is brimming with lean protein and slow-release carbohydrates, making it an ideal pre-gym snack to fuel your fat burning

INGREDIENTS

(SERVES 1)

1 seeded bagel

2tsp green pesto

30g mozzarella, sliced

50g cooked chicken breast, sliced

½ tomato, sliced

1tsp chopped basil leaves

TO MAKE

- Spread the pesto over the mozzarella slices.
- Cut the bagel in half and layer the ingredients evenly across it.
- Garnish with the basil.

Per portion Calories **183** / Protein **13g** / Fat **17g** / Carbs **5g**

THE BENEFITS

CHICKEN
provides pantothenic acid, which helps to metabolise fat.

MOZZARELLA
provides protein, which builds muscle.

PESTO
provides fibre, which fills you up.

AVOCADO BAKED EGGS

Take a break from scrambling or frying and make eggs even healthier by adding a decent hit of good fats alongside your muscle-building protein

INGREDIENTS

(SERVES 1)

1 large avocado, halved and stone removed

2 eggs

70g pancetta

Small handful of cress

Pepper to taste

TO MAKE

- Preheat the oven to 200°C/gas mark 6.
- Place the avocado halves in a casserole dish, cut sides up. Crack an egg into each hole left by the stone. Put the lid on the casserole dish and bake in the oven for eight minutes.
- Meanwhile lightly fry the pancetta in a non-stick pan over a medium heat for four to five minutes, stirring throughout, until crisp.
- Remove from the pan and place on kitchen roll to remove any excess oil.
- Take the avocado out of the oven. Sprinkle the cress, pepper and pancetta on top and serve.

Per portion Calories **566** / Protein **21g** / Fat **49g** / Carbs **18g**

THE BENEFITS

AVOCADO
provides fibre, which improves digestion.

PANCETTA
provides vitamin B6, which boosts energy levels.

EGG
provides zinc, which increases testosterone production.

HAM AND RED PEPPER OMELETTE

Few meals provide as much protein for as little effort as the humble omelette, especially when it's stuffed with muscle-building pork and casein-rich blue cheese

INGREDIENTS
(SERVES 1)

3 eggs
1tsp butter
75g ham hock, chopped
½ red pepper, diced
20g blue cheese, crumbled

TO MAKE
- Crack the eggs into a mixing jug. Add the ham, pepper and cheese and whisk.
- Heat the butter in a non-stick pan over a low heat.
- Pour the mixture into the pan. Cook until browned underneath, then place under a medium grill for two to three minutes until the top is cooked through.

Per portion Calories **444** / Protein **39g** / Fat **29g** / Carbs **4g**

THE BENEFITS

HAM HOCK
provides vitamin B2, which plays a key role in energy production.

RED PEPPER
provides vitamin E, which helps maintain healthy cholesterol levels.

BLUE CHEESE
provides casein, which helps to repair muscle tissue.

CHORIZO AND SCALLOP SKEWERS

Meat and seafood make an excellent muscle-building combo in this Spanish-style dish that takes minutes to prepare but provides your body with everything it needs for recovery

INGREDIENTS
(SERVES 2)

100g chorizo
150g scallops
70g edamame beans
2tsp olive oil

TO MAKE
- Split the oil evenly between two pans and heat both over a medium heat.
- Fry the chorizo in one pan and the scallops in the other for two to three minutes, turning to ensure they cook evenly on both sides.
- Skewer the chorizo and scallops and serve with the edamame beans.

Per portion Calories **788** / Protein **66g** / Fat **51g** / Carbs **9g**

THE BENEFITS

CHORIZO
provides iron, which generates energy.

SCALLOP
provides selenium, which improves sleep.

EDAMAME BEANS
provide vitamin K, which strengthens bones.

MACKEREL AND BEETROOT SALAD

Enhance your bedroom prowess with mackerel, a little-known libido-booster rich in energy-boosting iron and circulation-improving omega 3 fatty acids

INGREDIENTS

(SERVES 1)

2 smoked mackerel fillets
1 beetroot, ready cooked, cut into wedges
½ handful of coriander leaves
½ handful of watercress
1tsp lemon juice
1tbsp olive oil

TO MAKE

- Arrange the mackerel and beetroot on a plate.
- Garnish with the coriander and watercress.
- Drizzle the lemon juice and olive oil on top, and serve.

Per portion Calories **624** / Protein **44g** / Fat **45g** / Carbs **9g**

THE BENEFITS

BEETROOT
provides folate, which improves cardiovascular health.

CORIANDER
provides vitamin K, which strengthens bones.

WATERCRESS
provides vitamin C, which boosts immunity.

SESAME TUNA WITH SALSA SALAD

Give your seafood a spicy twist with this muscle-building tuna steak and salsa combo, which provides extra servings of fat-fighting chromium and metabolism-boosting potassium

INGREDIENTS
(SERVES 2)

2 x 150g tuna steaks
2tsp grated ginger
1 garlic clove, finely chopped
2tbsp dark soy sauce
1tbsp black sesame seeds
1tbsp white sesame seeds
1tbsp rapeseed oil

FOR THE SALSA
Handful of cherry
tomatoes, quartered
½ red onion, diced
1 garlic clove, finely chopped
¼ red pepper, diced
¼ yellow pepper, diced
2tbsp lemon juice
1tbsp olive oil
1tsp coriander
leaves, chopped
Salt and pepper to taste

TO MAKE
- Mix the ginger, garlic and soy sauce to create a marinade. Pour over the tuna and place to one side for five minutes.
- Mix all the salsa ingredients together and season.
- Remove the tuna from the marinade and roll in the sesame seeds.
- Heat the oil in a pan until hot. Cook the tuna for 30 seconds on each side.
- Slice the tuna and serve with the salsa.

Per portion Calories **687** / Protein **74g** / Fat **27g** / Carbs **31g**

THE BENEFITS

TUNA
provides zinc, which
boosts testosterone.

CHERRY TOMATO
provides vitamin C,
which strengthens ligaments
and tendons.

CORIANDER
provides manganese,
which helps maintain healthy
blood sugar levels.

SALMON TERIYAKI WITH CUCUMBER RIBBONS

If you want to pack on muscle, this should be your snack of choice – its high levels
of omega 3 fatty acids will help you recover fast after a tough workout

INGREDIENTS

(SERVES 1)

2 salmon fillets

1 cucumber

2tsp soy sauce

1tsp olive oil

2tsp dry sherry

1tsp caster sugar

1tsp grated ginger

1 garlic clove, finely chopped

1tsp rapeseed oil

TO MAKE

- Cut the cucumber into long, thin ribbons using a potato peeler.
- Mix the soy sauce, olive oil, sherry, caster sugar, ginger and garlic to make a glaze.
- Marinate the salmon in half the glaze mixture and the cucumber ribbons in the other half for at least three minutes.
- Fry the salmon in the rapeseed oil over a medium heat for three minutes on each side.
- Serve the salmon on top of the cucumber.

Per portion Calories **971** / Protein **37g** / Fat **43g** / Carbs **17g**

THE BENEFITS

SALMON
provides vitamin B12, which
boosts energy levels.

CUCUMBER
provides silica, which
reinforces ligaments
and tendons.

GARLIC
provides manganese, which
strengthens bones.

SALMON TARTARE

This healthy upgrade of the classic hors d'oeuvre recipe swaps blood sugar-spiking crackers for ultra-filling avocado slices to help combat hunger pangs and fight fat

INGREDIENTS

(SERVES 1)

100g salmon, finely diced
½tsp lemon zest
2tbsp black olives, finely chopped
½ avocado, sliced
A few lemon slices
Salt and pepper to taste

TO MAKE

- The salmon should be as fresh as possible. If you can only get pre-packed supermarket salmon, use smoked salmon instead to be on the safe side.
- Mix the salmon with lemon zest and salt and pepper.
- Garnish with the olives and serve with the avocado and lemon slices.

Per portion Calories **320** / Protein **22g** / Fat **23g** / Carbs **11g**

THE BENEFITS

SALMON
provides omega 3, which reduces inflammation.

BLACK OLIVES
provide copper, which strengthens bones.

AVOCADO
provides pantothenic acid, which plays a key role in energy production.

WHOLEMEAL BATTERED SCAMPI

There's no reason to save this classic crustacean snack for seaside resorts and basket-based restaurants, especially when it's so rich in protein and easy to prepare at home

INGREDIENTS

(SERVES 1)

200g raw king
prawns, peeled
75g wholemeal flour
100ml milk
2tbsp rapeseed oil
2tbsp diced gherkins
1tbsp diced shallots
1tsp chopped parsley
1tbsp capers
1tbsp mayonnaise
Juice of ½ lemon
½ bag of mixed salad leaves

TO MAKE

- Whisk the flour and milk together in a bowl.
- Dip the prawns in the mixture.
- Fry them in the oil in a deep pan for three to four minutes.
- Mix together the gherkins, shallots, parsley, capers, mayonnaise and lemon juice to make the tartare sauce.
- Serve the scampi on a bed of salad leaves, garnished with the sauce.

Per portion Calories **865** / Protein **46g** / Fat **50g** / Carbs **60g**

THE BENEFITS

PRAWN
provides selenium, which boosts immunity.

LEMON
provides vitamin C, which helps to keep joints healthy.

GHERKIN
provides silica, which strengthens ligaments and connective tissues.

CHILLI AND LIME TIGER PRAWNS

Team low-calorie, high-protein prawns with metabolism-boosting chilli to help you burn fat around the clock

INGREDIENTS

(SERVES 1)

150g tiger prawns
Juice of 1 lime
1 red chilli, sliced
Handful of fresh
coriander, chopped
1tbsp rapeseed oil

TO MAKE

- Heat the rapeseed oil in a pan over a medium heat and fry the prawns for four minutes, turning halfway through.
- Season the prawns with the lime juice, mix them in with the chilli and then garnish with the coriander.

Per portion Calories **340** / Protein **31g** / Fat **16g** / Carbs **14g**

THE BENEFITS

PRAWN
provides iodine, which is crucial for normal thyroid function.

LIME
provides vitamin C, which boosts immunity.

RED CHILLI
provides capsaicin, which has anti-inflammatory properties.

EGG, TOMATO AND BEAN SALAD

This protein-rich vegetarian-friendly salad is easy to make
and contains everything you need to pack on serious size

INGREDIENTS

(SERVES 1)

2 eggs
100g chickpeas
100g kidney beans
Handful of baby plum
tomatoes, halved
½ red chilli, thinly sliced
10g coriander leaves
1tbsp guacamole

TO MAKE

- Boil the eggs in water for ten minutes. Leave to cool, then remove the shells and cut in half.
- Toss the chickpeas, kidney beans, tomatoes, chilli and coriander leaves together. Top with the eggs and the guacamole.

Per portion Calories **448**/ Protein **29g** / Fat **17g** / Carbs **41g**

THE BENEFITS

EGG
provides vitamin B12,
which is important
for brain health.

CHICKPEAS
provide protein,
which helps to regulate
blood sugar.

KIDNEY BEANS
provide iron, which
boosts energy.

GOAT'S CHEESE AND BEETROOT COUSCOUS

Harness the energy-boosting, recovery-enhancing powers of beetroot
with this simple couscous recipe packed with the purple stuff

INGREDIENTS

(SERVES 1)

50ml boiling water
75g couscous
75g goat's cheese
½ cooked beetroot, sliced
Handful of baby spinach
leaves

TO MAKE

- Place the couscous in a medium bowl and the water over it. Mix well, cover and leave for five minutes.
- Fluff up the couscous with a fork, then add the goat's cheese, beetroot and spinach.

Per portion Calories **567** / Protein **27g** / Fat **23g** / Carbs **64g**

THE BENEFITS

BEETROOT
provides manganese, which
strengthens bones.

COUSCOUS
provides selenium,
which improves sleep.

BABY SPINACH
provides folate, which
improves nervous
system function.

SMOOTHIES

Blending nutritious ingredients into an easily downable drink is one of the simplest ways to fuel your fitness, whatever your training goals

BANANA AND AVOCADO

Improve the quality and quantity of your shut-eye with this creamy sleep-enhancing drink

Per portion Calories **561** / Protein **29g** / Fat **20g** / Carbs **77g**

INGREDIENTS
(SERVES 1)

1 banana
½ avocado
1 kiwi fruit
Handful of kale
400ml milk
1tbsp honey

THE BENEFITS

BANANA
provides tryptophan, which the body converts into serotonin and melatonin to promote soothing sleep.

AVOCADO
provides magnesium, which helps to calm your nervous system and prepare it for sleep.

KIWI FRUIT
provides antioxidants, which improve the onset, duration and quality of sleep.

KALE
helps the brain to use tryptophan more efficiently to improve sleep quality.

CHOCOLATE AND COCONUT

Harness the benefits of dark chocolate to help, not hinder, your muscle-building efforts

Per portion Calories **820** / Protein **22g** / Fat **38g** / Carbs **79g**

INGREDIENTS

(SERVES 1)

20g 85% dark chocolate

100g coconut milk

25g scoop whey protein isolate

1 pinch cinnamon

1 banana

50g raw oats, soaked in 100g water

THE BENEFITS

DARK CHOCOLATE
provides flavonoids, which supply
working muscles with oxygen.

COCONUT MILK
is calorie dense, containing 140kcal
per 100g to fuel muscle growth.

WHEY PROTEIN ISOLATE
provides protein to help build
and repair muscle tissue.

CINNAMON
improves insulin sensitivity
and body composition.

ORANGE AND CHILLI

Turn your body into a fat incinerator with this spicy, metabolism-boosting smoothie

Per portion Calories **196** / Protein **35g** / Fat **1g** / Carbs **14g**

INGREDIENTS

(SERVES 1)

Juice of 1 orange
Pinch of chilli powder
1 scoop of whey protein isolate
400ml green tea, cold
Handful of kale

THE BENEFITS

ORANGE
provides vitamin C, which helps to combat free radicals and improve recovery after training.

CHILLI
provides capsaicin, which also helps to suppress appetite.

WHEY PROTEIN ISOLATE
is very filling, helping you avoid the urge to snack.

GREEN TEA
provides the antioxidant ECGC, which causes an increase in fat oxidisation.

PEANUT BUTTER AND BANANA

This creamy smoothie provides plenty of muscle-building protein and abs-friendly healthy fats

Per portion Calories **401** / Protein**14g** / Fat **12g** / Carbs **63g**

INGREDIENTS

(SERVES 1)

1tsp peanut butter
1 banana
50g oats
1tbsp Greek yogurt
Pinch of ground ginger
Water, to taste

THE BENEFITS

PEANUT BUTTER
provides niacin, which will boost your energy levels ahead of a tough workout.

BANANA
provides vitamin B6, which helps the body break down and digest protein.

OATS
provide carbohydrate, which tops up your glycogen stores to fuel new muscle growth.

GREEK YOGURT
provides protein, which helps to build and repair muscle tissue.

STRAWBERRY AND CHILLI

Sweet and spicy, this berry-packed smoothie boasts an array of fat-fighting properties to get you lean

Per portion Calories **224** / Protein **7g** / Fat **3g** / Carbs **45g**

INGREDIENTS

(SERVES 1)

Handful of strawberries
Pinch of chilli powder
Handful of frozen raspberries
100ml natural yogurt
400ml cold green tea
Handful of kale

THE BENEFITS

STRAWBERRY
provides polyphenols, which help to improve blood sugar control and reduce fat storage.

CHILLI
provides capsaicin, which aids fat loss by increasing body temperature and energy expenditure.

RASPBERRY
provides fibre, which helps keep you full and avoid the temptation to snack.

NATURAL YOGURT
provides filling protein, which helps to minimise muscle wastage when eating for fat loss.

ORANGE AND CARROT

Boost your immune system with this potent germ-proofing citrus shake

Per portion Calories **559** / Protein **28g** / Fat **1g** / Carbs **115g**

INGREDIENTS

(SERVES 1)

2 carrots, peeled
1 orange, peeled
½ mango
125g probiotic Greek yogurt
250ml grape juice
Pinch of ginger

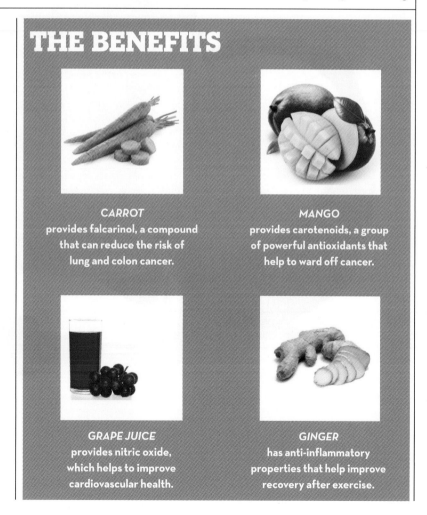

THE BENEFITS

CARROT
provides falcarinol, a compound that can reduce the risk of lung and colon cancer.

MANGO
provides carotenoids, a group of powerful antioxidants that help to ward off cancer.

GRAPE JUICE
provides nitric oxide, which helps to improve cardiovascular health.

GINGER
has anti-inflammatory properties that help improve recovery after exercise.

COCONUT AND COFFEE

Sharpen up with this caffeine-packed, focus-boosting pre-workout smoothie

Per portion Calories **278** / Protein **4g** / Fat **68g** / Carbs **0g**

INGREDIENTS

(SERVES 1)

300ml coconut water
1 shot of espresso
1 banana
Handful of blueberries
1 apple

THE BENEFITS

COCONUT WATER
contains a host of essential
brain-enhancing electrolytes.

COFFEE
is a stimulant that can help to delay
your perceptions of fatigue.

BLUEBERRY
provides antioxidants, which have
been shown to improve memory.

APPLE
has been found to reduce the
risk of brain diseases such as
Alzheimer's and Parkinson's.

CHOCOLATE AND BEETROOT

Go further and faster for longer with this endurance-boosting shake

Per portion Calories **381** / Protein **14g** / Fat **19g** / Carbs **44g**

INGREDIENTS

(SERVES 2)

2 squares of dark chocolate
1 small beetroot, peeled
300ml milk
50g strawberries
50g raspberries

THE BENEFITS

DARK CHOCOLATE
provides flavonoids, which help transfer oxygen to working muscles by keeping blood vessels healthy.

BEETROOT
can reduce the oxygen cost of aerobic exercise and increase the time it takes to reach exhaustion.

MILK
provides endurance-fuelling carbohydrates and electrolytes.

STRAWBERRY
can help to improve blood sugar control and avoid energy slumps.

KALE AND PEAR

Down a dose of fat-fighting veg with this phytonutrient-rich breakfast smoothie

Per portion Calories **143** / Protein **2g** / Fat **1g** / Carbs **36g**

INGREDIENTS

(SERVES 1)

Handful of kale
½ pear
1 scoop of natural yogurt
Pinch of cinnamon
1tbsp honey
Water, to taste

THE BENEFITS

KALE
provides calcium, which plays a key role in regulating body fat levels.

PEAR
provides anti-inflammatory flavonoids, which help you recover after a fat-torching gym session.

NATURAL YOGURT
provides high levels of protein to keep you feeling full throughout the morning.

HONEY
has been found to increase exercise capacity during workouts, allowing you to burn more calories.

EGGNOG

Enjoy this festive muscle-building cocktail all year round
– added bourbon very much optional

Per portion Calories **157** / Protein **8g** / Fat **7g** / Carbs **16g**

INGREDIENTS
(SERVES 4)

450ml milk
3 eggs, whisked
50g honey
1tsp orange zest, grated
2tsp vanilla extract
A pinch of nutmeg

THE BENEFITS

MILK
provides calcium, which helps
your body to metabolise
fat more efficiently.

EGG
provides a full set
of amino acids to help
with building muscle.

NUTMEG
helps to reduce and soothe muscle
inflammation after training.

VANILLA EXTRACT
provides antioxidants, which help to
combat free radicals in the body.

100 WAYS TO COOK LIKE A PRO

1 BOWLED OVER

To peel garlic more easily, use two bowls the same size. Put the garlic cloves in one bowl, place the other one on top and press down to crush the cloves. Shake vigorously to release the skins.

Rob Bragagnolo, Marben

2 SCRUB UP

Scrub vegetables rather than peeling them – that way you preserve the skin, which contains lots of nutrients.

**Steve Pidgeon,
The Arundell Arms**

3 SWEETEN UP

Cook onions slowly to draw out their natural sweetness. Once they've browned in the pan, turn down the heat and stir frequently for 20-30 minutes – you won't need sugar.

Oliver Gladwin, The Shed

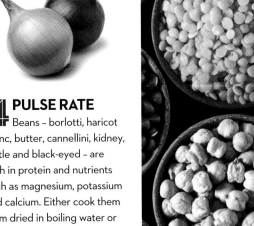

4 PULSE RATE

Beans – borlotti, haricot blanc, butter, cannellini, kidney, turtle and black-eyed – are high in protein and nutrients such as magnesium, potassium and calcium. Either cook them from dried in boiling water or open a tin, rinse and throw into a salad. You can use them to replace rice or potato, or crush

them with olive oil, lemon zest and garlic for a tasty dip. When cooking dried kidney beans, soak them first and boil for half an hour to remove toxins.
Anna Haugh-Kelly, London House

5 SOUP UP YOUR SALADS

Substitute pancetta for nuts and seeds in salads. When making a Caesar salad, instead of adding fried pancetta, try pumpkin seeds and Marcona almonds. Both add protein, essential oils and vitamins, and they provide a meaty punch.
Andy Cook, The Savoy Grill

6 BAKE HERBS

Parsley, coriander and mint can be dried in a cooling oven, crumbled and sprinkled on food before serving.
Tony Kitous, Comptoir Libanais

7 FINE TUNA

Look for interesting dried ingredients such as dehydrated balsamic vinegar, smoked paprika, powdered seawater – yes, you can get this – and kombu dashi. Mixing these together can lift the flavour of a fresh tuna steak or turkey escalope when used as a dry rub marinade. Dry-fry in a non-stick pan for an intense taste.
Antony Bennett, La Tasca

8 SALT EARLY

Salt matures during the cooking process, so to ensure food is healthier and to use less make sure you add it at the outset. For example, if a recipe calls for 20g of salt and you seasoned your dish towards the end rather than at the start, you would need 30g for the finished creation to taste the same.
Joseph Woodland, Barnyard

9 USE FLOUR POWER

Use chickpea flour for batter – it's gluten free and high in protein. To make our classic pakoras we use a batter made from chickpea flour, water, cumin seeds, turmeric, salt, chillies and coriander. Use it to coat spinach and onions and deep-fry in small balls, tempura style.
Raju Rawat, Zumbura

10 SLOW DOWN

Take your time – eating too quickly forces air into the digestive tract where it can get trapped, causing your stomach to bloat. Chewing each mouthful thoroughly produces enzymes that start to break down fats, simple sugars and starches, so your food reaches your stomach in a more manageable form. This cuts down on fermentation in the gut and reduces the production of gas.
Jeff Tyler, Novikov

RAISE YOUR STEAKS

A good steak is one of the most fundamental things you can learn to cook – and it's all about heat. Consultant chef Colin Bussey (colinbussey.com) explains the form

11 CHOOSE THE BEST MEAT

To cook a great steak, you have to start with the best ingredients. Buy your beef from a reputable butcher rather than a supermarket for the best quality. Ideally you want a 21-day hung rib-eye steak, nicely marbled and at least 3.5cm thick so it stays juicy when cooked.

12 USE THE RIGHT OIL

Heat a heavy-bottomed pan and add around 20ml of cold-pressed extra virgin rapeseed oil per steak. This oil is high in omega 3s and vitamin E, and doesn't become unstable at high temperatures as olive oil does. Add garlic, rosemary and thyme to the pan too.

13 SEAR YOUR STEAK FIRST

Season the meat to your liking and place it in the hot pan, searing it for 30 seconds on each side to brown the meat and give it a rich, nutty flavour. You should then transfer it in an oven dish and place it in an oven heated to 180°C/gas mark 4 for three to four minutes to keep it pink and ensure it's evenly cooked.

14 LEAVE IT TO REST

Once the meat is cooked, remove the steak from the oven and leave it to rest on a warm plate for four to five minutes before serving so that the meat has time to relax. If you don't do this, the blood will run out as soon as you cut into it.

15 MAKE A CLEAN CUT

Use a high-quality straight-edged steak knife to cut cleanly into the meat. A typical serrated knife will tear at it, undoing all the good work you've put into cooking the meat to succulent perfection.

16 PEARL ONE OUT

Most risottos are cheesy, creamy and very calorific. For a healthier version, replace your fancy arborio risotto rice with pearl barley and use the same cooking process.
Danny Brown, Flava-It

17 GO NUTS

Use coconut oil instead of butter or oil in recipes – it helps to lower cholesterol, boosts immunity and enhances the flavours of the food.
Tom Aikens, Tom's Kitchen

18 BAKE WITH SALT

We salt-bake a lot of our vegetables before blending them for soup. It helps us to avoid adding extra butter, oil or salt, and it concentrates the flavour. Bake a butternut squash in its skin on a bed of sea salt, then peel and blend (not the salt) with vegetable stock for a creamy soup.
Andy Cook, The Savoy Grill

19 HEAT YOUR MEAT

Apart from tiny things such as squid, prawns and so on, protein cooks better if it's at room temperature first.
Jacob Kennedy, Bocca Di Lupo

20 SQUIDS IN

To tenderise squid, cover it with milk and chopped kiwi or pineapple. Store it in the fridge overnight, then rinse and dry thoroughly. The fruit enzymes will break down the meat perfectly.
Rob Bragagnolo, Marben

21 YOU'LL LIKE THIS SHALLOT

Add finely chopped shallots to salad dressing. Vinegar loves shallots, and they

add great flavour and a bit of bite. They're the secret ingredient in my classic French vinaigrette, but I add it to all my dressings.
Judy Joo, Jinjuu

22 SWEETEN NATURALLY

Use ground almonds, eggs and honey as natural sweeteners, and for garnishing desserts. Tasty *and* healthy.
Russell Ford, 108 Pantry, Marylebone Hotel

23 PURPLE POWER

When you've got the oven on for something else, bake some aubergines until tender, then freeze or store in the fridge for another meal.
Tony Kitous, Comptoir Libanais

24 JUST ADD WATER

Soak raw almonds to eat as a snack or add to your favourite food. Soaking nuts makes the proteins more readily available for absorption.
Shirin Kouros, The Good Life Eatery

25 THINK FRESH

Add fresh herbs, such as basil, coriander and mint, to salads to add a punchy flavour – and some extra all-important nutrients.
Caroline Mili Artiss, The Gorgeous Kitchen

26 MASTER THE ROUX

Instead of adding heavy cream to a sauce to make it thick and creamy, make a roux with gluten-free flour and almond milk. It works brilliantly.
Shirin Kouros, The Good Life Eatery

27 STAY SHARP

Use the back of a plate to sharpen your knife. Place your knife at a 20° angle on the ceramic ring on the bottom of a plate, then slide the blade back and forth five or six times per side. It will be remarkably sharper.
Rob Bragagnolo, Marben

28 REDUCE IRRITATION

If you have a sensitive gut, avoid onions, garlic and leeks – which contain fermentable carbohydrates called fructans. Instead of these, use the green, leafy parts of spring onions, leeks and chives to flavour your recipes.
Dr Joan Ransley, loveyourgut.com

29 STOP SMOKING

If you need a very hot pan to cook something such as a steak, add your oil after the pan has been heated to the required temperature or the oil will burn.

**Shirin Kouros,
The Good Life Eatery**

30 GET THE PAPERS

Cooking *en papilotte* – inside paper – is a great way to cook fish and vegetables, and avoids oily frying and baking. Cook organic salmon with fennel and summer squash, and enhance the flavours with fresh basil and lemon. The paper envelope keeps all the flavours together so you lose none of the healthy fats from the fish or the nutrients from the veg.

Andy Cook, The Savoy Grill

31 SOAK AND SERVE

If you perfect the art of making marinades, your meat will taste so good you won't need a rich sauce or dressing. Blitz lemongrass, ginger, garlic, spring onions, coriander, salt and olive oil together in a blender for a perfect Asian-style marinade.

**Caroline Mili Artiss,
The Gorgeous Kitchen**

32 REDUCE STEAM

Never season fish before you cook it as it will draw the water to the surface and create steam. That's why you don't get a crisp skin. Also, if you don't want to smell of fish, always wear disposable plastic gloves while preparing it.

**Andrew Turner,
Hotel Café Royal**

33 DITCH THE SPUDS

Cut out starch by using root veg instead of potatoes in your Sunday roast. As a bonus, the sugars in root vegetables caramelise and bring a natural jammy goodness to your roast.

Danny Brown, Flava-It

34 CROUT-OFF

Swap the croutons in soups for a mixture of pine nuts, chopped spring onions, chopped chilli and fresh basil for added taste and texture.

Andy Cook, The Savoy Grill

35 USE THE SHOULDER

Pork shoulder, or blade, is very versatile. It can be fried, or slow-roasted for as long as six hours. Cook it with apples and carrots.

Allan Pickett, Plateau

36 NICE CUBES

Freeze cubes of lamb or beef to make kebabs. Coat them in yogurt before freezing – it will make them more tender when you thaw and then grill them.

**Tony Kitous,
Comptoir Libanais**

BE A YOLK HERO

Gleneagles head chef Alan Gibb helps you unleash shell

37 MIX MASTERY

To improve your scramble, stir the beaten eggs continuously while cooking until they're just starting to firm up, then take them off the heat and stir in a little cream, butter or – for Turkish-style eggs – Greek yogurt.

38 OMELETTE IT BE

For a good omelette, heat the butter until it's frothy and add the egg. As it starts to set, lean the pan at an angle, fold the top edge over and transfer to a warmed plate.

39 FLAWLESS FRYING

For perfect fried eggs, remove them from the heat when the whites are nearly set, add 2tsp of boiling water, cover with a lid and steam for one minute. They're great with grilled asparagus spears.

40 PERFECT POACHING

A splash of white wine vinegar will keep your eggs together – but to stop them being watery, remove them from the pan with a slotted spoon and drain them on kitchen paper. Serve with spinach and nutmeg.

41 BETTER BOILING

Make sure your eggs are at room temperature, bring the water to the boil and then turn it down to a simmer. Cook the eggs for 12 minutes, then cool. To shell them, leave them in a fridge for two hours, then roll them on a counter top.

TOOL UP

Michelin-starred chef Adam Gray's top bits of kit

42 THE KNIFE

'A sharp, medium-sized chopping knife is the first thing you should buy. Sharpen it regularly.'
GRAY'S PICK I.O.Shen 24cm chef's knife
£99.95 *ioshen.co.uk*

43 THE BOARD

'Use high-density plastic rather than wood for hygiene. Coloured boards make it easy to keep raw meat and vegetables apart.'
GRAY'S PICK Joseph Joseph Index Advance colour coded chopping board set
£48 *amazon.co.uk*

44 THE FRYING PAN

'Get a heavy, non-stick or cast-iron frying pan with a metal handle, so you can put it in the oven. These also retain an even heat.'
GRAY'S PICK GreenPan Michel Roux 24cm non-stick frying pan £70 *amazon.co.uk*

45 THE SAUCEPAN

'A deep-bottomed saucepan will set you up for casseroles, soups and sauces. A good-quality pan may set you back £50-£70, but it will last.'
GRAY'S PICK GreenPan Michel Roux 16cm saucepan
£65 *amazon.co.uk*

46 THE 'SPOON'

'A high-heat rubber spatula is ideal for stirring soups, sauces or eggs. Much better than a wooden spoon.'
GRAY'S PICK Vogue High Heat Spatula
£5.99 *nisbets.co.uk*

47 THE TURNER

'You also want a stainless steel slotted fish spatula for turning delicate fish or grilled vegetables.'
GRAY'S PICK Wusthof Silverpoint Slotted Turner
£21.32 *russums-shop.co.uk*

48 THE TONGS

'A pair of good-quality metal tongs is handy for more than just the barbecue. Use them to turn meat in a frying pan.'
GRAY'S PICK Professional Tongs £3.36 *russums-shop.co.uk*

49 THE GRINDER

'Small spice grinders are fantastic for your own spice blends, fresh coffee beans and quick dips.'
GRAY'S PICK Cuisinart Electric Spice and Nut Grinder
£42 *hartsofstur.com*

50 THE GRATER

'A micro-grater makes grating anything from parmesan to ginger easy.'
GRAY'S PICK Microplane Premium Zester-Grater
£17.95 *amazon.co.uk*

51 THE BLENDER

'An electric hand blender is perfect for making soups and smoothies.'
GRAY'S PICK Kenwood Hand Blender HB711M
£34.99 *amazon.co.uk*

52 THE TRAY

'Buy a cast-iron or heavy stainless steel roasting tray. Flimsy ones may buckle.'
GRAY'S PICK Le Creuset Roasting Pan 35cm
£139 *richmondcookshop.co.uk*

53 THE PEELER

'A speed peeler is much than a traditional one. Peeling veg will be a pleasure.'
GRAY'S PICK Kuhn Rikon Original Swiss Peeler
£3.84 *amazon.co.uk*

54 GREEN GOLD

One of the most popular dishes on the summer menu at La Fosse is our chicken with green salad – peas, spinach and broad beans. It's packed with nutrients and antioxidants, and tastes great.

**Mark Hartstone,
La Fosse**

55 PICK AT IT

Use a toothpick to check that your fish is cooked. If you can insert it easily into the thickest part of the flesh, it's cooked perfectly. Any resistance means it needs a little more time.

**Gee Charman,
The Gorgeous Kitchen**

56 HAPPY ENDINGS

Like cut flowers, fresh herbs benefit from having their stalk ends cut and placed in cold water to freshen the leaves.

**Tony Kitous,
Comptoir Libanais**

57 LIQUID ASSET

When poaching or steaming – which are the healthiest ways to cook – flavour the liquid first. Throw in aromatics, herbs and spices. These will infuse through the water and steam, making whatever you're cooking more fragrant and flavourful.

Judy Joo, Jinjuu

58 SUPER SOAKER

Use acidic marinades to make meat tender. Marinate small cuts for one to 24 hours, or big ones for one to two days, in a yogurt- or lemon juice-based marinade. It's especially good for barbecuing.

**Jacob Kennedy,
Bocca Di Lupo**

59 FLAX IS BACK

Use these little seeds to ramp up your protein intake whenever you can. Ground flax seeds can be added to a basic dhal curry for a host of health benefits.

Danny Brown, Flava-It

60 EVENING DRESS

When adding a dressing to salad leaves, drizzle it around the inside edge of a mixing bowl, then add your salad and toss together. This will ensure a lighter and more even coating than you would achieve by pouring it on top of the leaves.

**Jo Pratt, The
Gorgeous Kitchen**

61 THE THIGHS HAVE IT

When properly seasoned and cooked at a high heat, chicken thighs release any excess fat and crisp up, giving you all the flavour and none of the health downsides. Sprinkle them with salt before cooking.

Lee Bennett, Crafthouse

62 PAPER BAKED

Use baking parchment or silicon paper – not greaseproof paper – in the bottom of your frying pan. You'll need next to no fat in the pan, nothing will stick and your meat will colour nicely.

Bernhard Engelhardt, Suchef

63 SPELT CORRECTLY

Use flour made from spelt – also known as dinkel wheat – as a healthier alternative to gluten-laden white flour when making a sweet or savoury recipe.

Danny Brown, Flava-It

64 SALT, DON'T SWEETEN

Trying to remove bitterness? A pinch of salt often works better than sugar – especially when you're using dark chocolate.

Rob Bragagnolo, Marben

65 GO WITH THE GRAIN

Mustard is a fantastic ingredient because it adds plenty of flavour without contributing a lot of calories. You can use it to marinate proteins, add it to dressings and put it in sauces. It's a versatile ingredient that can make everything zestier and more interesting.

Judy Joo, Jinjuu

66 PALM OIL

When chopping chillies, rub a little cooking

oil into your hands before you start. The oil creates a barrier so the chilli doesn't get into your skin. Then, once you've chopped the chillies, rub some fresh lemon juice into your hands – the acid neutralises the chilli, removing it from your hands more effectively than soap and water.
Jo Pratt, The Gorgeous Kitchen

67 BAG IT UP
When using skinless chicken breast or any other lean meat, try cooking it *sous-vide* by placing it in a vacuum bag in a water bath at low temperature of 55-64°C for about 45 minutes. This will reduce shrinkage of the meat while retaining all the nutrients, flavour and goodness.
Bernhard Engelhardt, Suchef

68 LEAN OUT
Lean protein lends itself to lean cooking. Steaks and white meats such as veal, pork, chicken, rabbit and fish are ideal for grilling, searing, poaching and roasting.
Jacob Kennedy, Bocca Di Lupo

69 FACE FACTS
Pork cheeks are widely used in restaurants but not at home. Season them and throw them in a casserole dish for a few hours for a cheap, tasty meal.
Lee Bennett, Crafthouse

70 STEAM AHEAD
Use a steamer rather than boiling vegetables in water as most nutrients are lost in the water when boiling.
Shirin Kouros, The Good Life Eatery

71 LIQUID SENSE
When boiling beans, flavour the cooking liquid. I like to use a crushed garlic clove, half a peeled onion, two bay leaves and half a fresh chilli. Once the beans are cooked, drain them and discard the aromatics.
Tony Kitous, Comptoir Libanais

72 REST FOR SUCCESS
Lean meats tend to dry out more easily while cooking, so it's important that you rest them afterwards to distribute the juice through the meat. As a rule, rest your meat for one minute per 100g. Cover big cuts loosely in foil to stop them getting cold.
Gee Charman, The Gorgeous Kitchen

73 POP A CHERRY
To stop vegetables drying out while you're roasting them, throw a load of super-ripe cherry tomatoes over the top of them halfway through cooking. The juices from the bursting tomatoes will blend with the water from the

vegetables and make some seriously concentrated tasty pan juices that you can drizzle over the top of the final dish.
Antony Bennett, La Tasca

74 PORK OUT
For better bacon, bring it to room temperature before cooking, then put it in a frying pan before you turn on the heat. This will ensure the bacon heats up slowly, maximising the amount of fat rendered out of the bacon.
Theresa Gilliam, Bacon

75 PEEL GOOD
Use a spoon to peel ginger. The skin comes off easily and you'll waste less flesh than you would with a knife or peeler.
Rob Bragagnolo, Marben

76 BRING IT UP
When cooking steak, allow the meat to come up to room temperature for 30 minutes before cooking. Season with smoked Maldon sea salt when grilling.
Allan Picket, Plateau

77 DON'T CHILL

Keep tomatoes out of the fridge or they'll be floury.
**Shirin Kouros,
The Good Life Eatery**

78 FLIP IT

When roasting a whole bird, turn it upside down when it's finished cooking and pierce the breast cavity from the inside. The juices will go into the breast meat.
**Andrew Turner,
Hotel Café Royal**

79 HEAT YOUR GREENS

Most greens – including sugar snap peas, mange tout, fine beans, tender stem broccoli and spring greens – should be sautéed from raw in a very hot pan with coconut oil and cooked very quickly to maintain their crunch and goodness. Season with Maldon salt flakes and cracked black pepper.
Taher Jibet, The Dining Room

80 WAIT IT OUT

Season fish at least 15 minutes before cooking to firm up the flesh
**Jacob Kennedy,
Bocca Di Lupo**

81 EASY BUTTER

Make a simple herb butter by mixing chopped herbs with soft butter. You can then use this when grilling meat, fish and vegetables, basting them with it while they cook.
**Tony Kitous,
Comptoir Libanais**

82 JUST ADD NUTS

For creamy-tasting porridge, bread and vegetable pâtés, use sunflower seeds and walnuts that have been soaked overnight. They add texture and nutrients to dishes.
**Dr Joan Ransley,
loveyourgut.com**

83 IN CIDER TRADING

If you want to eat the skin of fruits and vegetables, wash them in apple cider vinegar rather than water to remove more dirt – and bugs.
**Shirin Kouros,
The Good Life Eatery**

84 DRESS TO IMPRESS

Blanch herbs in salted boiling water for 20 seconds, then put them straight into iced water, dry them and put them in a blender with a pinch of salt, the juice of two lemons and a glug of rapeseed oil. This dressing will last for days in an airtight container.
Danny Brown, Flava-It

85 PAN FOR GOLD

Invest in a quality non-stick pan. You can add a tiny drop of olive oil or low-calorie spray and dry-fry most ingredients, such as chicken breast, up to a point. Then add a tablespoon of intense stock, citrus fruit or seasoning, put a lid on and steam-fry to drive in flavour. Serve with salad and drizzle over the leftover liquid.
Antony Bennett, La Tasca

86 BRINE POWER

To keep pork and poultry moist, brine it. Use a mixture of salt, sugar (or honey or treacle) and water in a ratio of 1:1:10 by volume. Brine small cuts of meat for a few hours and larger cuts or whole birds for a day or two before cooking.
**Jacob Kennedy,
Bocca Di Lupo**

87 CRACK ON

Break eggs on a blunt surface instead of an edge to avoid damaging the egg and getting bits of shell in your food.
Rob Bragagnolo, Marben

88 CZECH PLEASE

If you have a beer with your meal, choose Czech or German – they contain far fewer additives.
Karol Gladki, karolgladki.com

89 GO HOT TURKEY

Use minced turkey as a low-fat alternative to minced beef. Try my Asian-style meatballs – add a generous amount of chopped garlic, ginger, chilli, coriander, a dash of fish sauce and an egg to minced turkey, season well and roll them up.
Caroline Mili Artiss, The Gorgeous Kitchen

90 NECK IT

Chicken necks are full of flavour and contain little fat. Use in stocks and soups.
David Philpot, Paternoster Chop House

91 WHITE OFF

Swap white sauces made with cream, mayonnaise and butter for low-fat pesto, tomato and pepper tapenades and vinegar-based dressings.
Antony Bennett, La Tasca

BOOST YOUR VEG INTAKE
Eating colourful veg isn't a chore. Get your five-a-day rainbow in minutes

92 REFUEL WITH... MANGO

Blend a ripe mango, two large bananas, a scoop of unflavoured whey protein, some crushed ice and 1tbsp coconut oil for a post-workout treat.
Anthea McCourtie, younutritionaltherapy.co.uk

93 TAN WITH... BROCCOLI

As well as its many other health benefits, broccoli contains glucoraphanin, which may prevent sun damage to the skin. Stir-fry in sesame oil and season with a splash of soy sauce.
Gurpareet Bains, gurpareetbains.co.uk

94 FUEL WITH... CHERRIES

Montmorency cherry concentrate mixed with water and some electrolytes makes an antioxidant-packed training drink. Too sour? Add some to a smoothie instead.
Anthea McCourtie, younutritionaltherapy.co.uk

95 DETOX WITH... CHICORY

This helps to purify the blood and contains antioxidant carotenes, as well as being low in calories. Place a spoonful of mackerel pâté into the leaf as a snack or healthy canapé.
Sam Bourne, foodspa.org.uk

96 SNACK ON... KALE

Rub the juice of half a lemon, 1tbsp olive oil and some sea salt into a bag of kale. Spread on a baking tray and bake at 140°C/gas mark 1 for 35 minutes, turning occasionally for a great snack.
Anthea McCourtie, younutritionaltherapy.co.uk

97 PREVENT DIABETES WITH... SWEET POTATO

Fry cumin seeds in olive oil until they start to pop, then drizzle over steamed sweet potato. Compounds in sweet potato can increase levels of adiponectin, which aids glucose regulation.
Gurpareet Bains, gurpareetbains.co.uk

98 GET HEALTHY WITH... SPINACH

Rich in vitamins and minerals, spinach is also packed with carotenoids and flavonoids for powerful antioxidant protection. Blanch in a frying pan with garlic and olive oil, and toss in Greek yogurt when cool.
Gurpareet Bains, gurpareetbains.co.uk

99 IMPROVE GUT-HEALTH WITH... BEETROOT

Support your friendly gut bacteria by eating roasted fresh beetroot. Dice and mix with rocket, pomegranate seeds and balsamic and olive oil dressing.
Elaine Jackson, connectingnutrition.co.uk

100 RECOVER WITH... CAULIFLOWER

Simmer until soft, then place in a blender and blitz into a soup. Add a dash of lemon juice and season to taste – it's an excellent source of vitamin K.
Gurpareet Bains, gurpareetbains.co.uk

A to Z

OF SUPPLEMENTS

Everything you need to know about nutritional supplements

Even if you're serious about fitness, you don't *have* to take supplements – you can get the nutrients you need to build a great body from healthy food like the meals in this book. But if you're short of time, supplements are a fast and convenient way to support your nutrition plan. They'll help you maximise your training gains and develop lean muscle, as well as improving your overall health. Here's our guide to some of the key supplements.

ARGININE

This non-essential amino acid is produced naturally in the body and improves performance by increasing nitric oxide production. Nitric oxide is a powerful vasodilator, which means it widens your blood vessels, increasing blood flow to the muscles and enabling better delivery of nutrients and oxygen to promote muscle recovery and growth during weights sessions. These effects are most beneficial for beginners.

BETA-ALANINE

This amino acid is great for improving your levels of focus and concentration during workouts or sports that require repeated sprints or bursts of power. It also increases concentration of the dipeptide carnosine in muscle, which allows you to perform more reps during intense weightlifting sessions. Make sure you stick to the label guidelines for dosage and take it on training days roughly 30 minutes before your workout.

BCAAS

Branched-chain amino acids, or BCAAs, are made up of three essential amino acids: leucine, isoleucine and valine. Leucine activates the complex compound mTOR, which is responsible for elevating muscle protein synthesis and subsequently muscle growth. Leucine also increases insulin production, which will help to shuttle those all-important muscle-building proteins to your cells post-workout. Valine combats another amino acid called tryptophan that's associated with muscle fatigue, which you definitely don't want. It reduces the uptake of tryptophan across the blood-brain barrier, which helps to keep you lifting harder and longer.

Look for a BCAA product with a high leucine content, ideally on a 4-1-1 or at least 2-1-1 ratio to maximise its benefits. Aim to take 10,000mg per day on training days, half directly before and half immediately after your session.

CAFFEINE

Commonly consumed in coffee and tea, this powerful stimulant affects the central and peripheral nervous system increasing the level of hormone-like endorphins in the brain, which reduce the perception of pain and fatigue and help to increase alertness and concentration. Caffeine has also been found

CASEIN

Casein is a form of protein commonly found in dairy products – it makes up around 80% of cow's milk, for example. It's a slow-release protein because it takes longer for your body to digest it, so you get more of a 'drip-feed' effect of protein into your bloodstream over a longer period. This makes it unsuitable for taking immediately after your workout when you need an instant hit, but ideal for consuming before bed. Take it in a shake with water before turning in for the night. This means your muscles will receive quality protein while you sleep, which is when they are repaired and rebuilt.

to increase muscle fibre recruitment to enhance performance during anaerobic exercises, although previous claims about its effectiveness as a fat-burner have been disproved.

Caffeine supplements come in pill or capsule form, and should be taken 30-60 minutes before exercise in accordance with packaging instructions.

CLA

A naturally occurring fatty acid, conjugated linoleic acid diverts calories away from fat storage and into muscle tissue, reducing body fat and increasing the amount of fat used for energy. It's also a non-stimulant-based supplement, making it ideal for those who want to avoid other fat burners containing caffeine or thermogenics.

CREATINE

Your body metabolises creatine into ATP, which is used for every initial muscle movement. It's therefore vital to have adequate supplies during heavy, high-intensity workouts to deliver the required energy to your muscles. In other words, creatine is like a backup generator for your muscles that helps you lift harder for longer.

Take 2-10g in your post-workout shake to replenish lost stores, or split your dose and have half before your workout and half after.

And make sure you drink plenty of water: creatine is hygroscopic, so it will suck water into your muscles and can leave you dehydrated.

ENERGY BARS AND GELS

These usually consist of maltodextrin – a carbohydrate derived from starch – and simple sugars such as fructose and glucose. Gels may also contain caffeine and electrolytes such as sodium and potassium. Both are designed to offer a convenient way of consuming carbs during bouts of endurance-based exercise lasting longer than an hour, after which your body's stores of glycogen will have been depleted.

Aim to ingest one to two bars or gels – each containing between 30g and 60g of sugar – per subsequent hour of exercise after you pass the 60-minute mark.

FISH OIL

This oil contains omega 3, an essential fatty acid that isn't produced in the body, which is why it's so important to supplement it in your diet. Taking a supplement can also help you to maintain a good omega 3 to omega 6 ratio – modern humans, as a rule, consume far too much omega 6. More specifically,

studies have shown that fish oil supplementation results in decreased body fat and reduced inflammation. It has also been linked to increased serotonin levels, more focus in training and less stress.

Take a spoonful with your meals. Most authorities recommend 1-4g a day, depending on how much oily fish is already in your diet.

GLUCOSAMINE

One of the major components of cartilage, glucosamine is an amino sugar that helps to cushion and absorb shock through our joints. As you age your cartilage gradually loses its elasticity and becomes less effective at protecting your joints, which can lead to injury. Glucosamine capsules and tablets – which tend to be made from lobster, crab and shrimp shells – combat this deterioration by stimulating the cartilage cells to produce proteoglycans, which help to restore joint function and mobility. Aim for three daily doses of 500mg.

GLUTAMINE

This amino acid should already be present in your body. However, if you have problems with your digestion or are training hard, a supplement can be helpful to strengthen the lining of your gut and help protein synthesis.

You have several options on how you take it, depending on your goals. Take 10g in

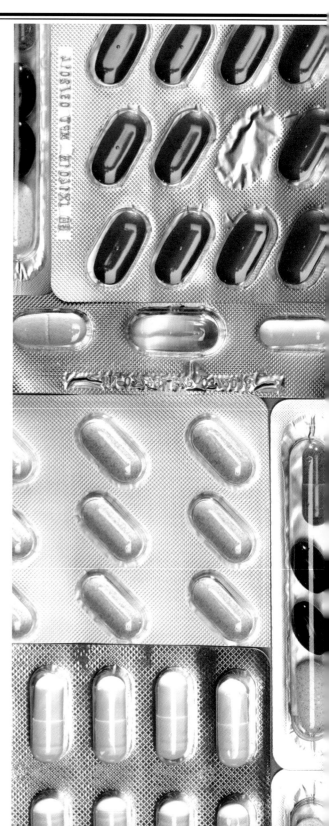

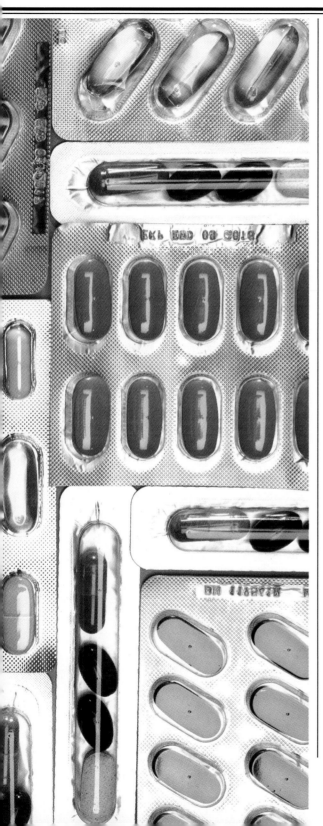

water on an empty stomach before breakfast to aid in gut healing and function, or 10g post-workout to replenish your stores. If you're on a low-carb diet, take 30g after your workout.

GREEN TEA

This tea – which originates from China and is produced using the leaves of the *Camellia sinensis* plant – is one of the best natural fat burners around. Green tea is also packed full of antioxidants and has been linked to the prevention of everything from heart disease to Alzheimer's. To reap the huge variety of health benefits, drink it in on a daily basis in place of your regular cup of tea or soft drink.

LEUCINE

As the most anabolic – or muscle-building – amino acid, leucine can independently stimulate insulin secretion and muscle protein synthesis, enhancing the muscle-building process. At 11%, whey protein is high in leucine content, which is one reason it's so effective as a post-workout elixir.

A 5g dose after training and between meals can increase the anabolic effect of food, especially when consuming protein sources that are low in leucine and which therefore might not stimulate maximum muscle protein synthesis on their own.

MULTIVITAMINS

A high-quality multivitamin can go a long way, and if you have to choose only one supplement it would make sense to go for this one as it will ensure you're getting the widest variety of vitamins and minerals possible. Of

L-CARNITINE

This compound, primarily found in red meat, plays many roles in the body, specifically in helping to use fat stores as fuel. Carn-Enhanced is a convenient liquid form that also contains vitamins B5 and B12 to increase your fat-burning potential and improve energy levels. Aim to take 500mg per day.

course, a multivitamin won't supply the same amount of individual minerals as products dedicated to these nutrients, but if your budget is tight it's a great safety net when it comes to overall health and wellbeing. Take two capsules a day, one with breakfast and one with lunch.

PROBIOTICS

Probiotics are live 'healthy' bacteria that live in our gut. They play a crucial role in maintaining optimum digestion, immunity and intestinal health by crowding out disease-causing bacteria and restoring the balance of intestinal flora. While you can buy probiotics in capsule form, a more economical alternative is to consume them via live yogurt drinks. A typical 125g yogurt provides 4 billion bacteria. Aim to consume one yogurt a day.

VITAMIN D

This vitamin is produced by the body when the skin comes into contact with sunlight. A lack of regular, strong sunlight in the UK means most Britons are severely lacking in this crucial vitamin that supports bone health and a strong immune system. Many studies also suggest that vitamin D may decrease risk for many diseases and conditions, including certain types of cancer, multiple sclerosis and hypertension, as well as aid in weight loss and even

VITAMIN C

One of the most well-known nutritional supplements, vitamin C is a water-soluble vitamin that occurs naturally in fruit and vegetables. It plays a key role in a variety of bodily functions, including the formation of connective tissue, the production of hormones such as adrenaline and the formation of red blood cells. Vitamin C is also a powerful antioxidant, helping to protect against cell damage, enhancing post-workout recovery and protecting against injury and illness. Daily doses of less than 1,000mg may be beneficial during periods of stress or intense training, but higher doses than this may hinder rather than help performance by blunting the muscles' ability to adapt to exercise.

improve longevity. Aim to take at least 1,000mg per day.

WHEY PROTEIN

Whey protein is made from cow's milk and comes in different forms, such as isolate, concentrate and hydrolysate. Whey is rapidly and easily absorbed, making it ideal to take during the critical post-workout window when your body is primed for muscle synthesis. It can also lower hunger levels owing to its influence on the hormone ghrelin.

Take whey protein within ten minutes of your workout to take advantage of the temporary rise in protein synthesis. If you're vegan or dairy intolerant, alternatives are available. Just avoid sugar-packed versions. Aim to take 25g blended with 200ml water immediately after training.

ZMA

ZMA combines zinc, magnesium and asparate, as well as vitamin B6. The first two play key roles in performance, enhancing cell growth and testosterone production and improving energy production while reducing levels of lactic acid and the perception of fatigue. Taking ZMA will help to correct common deficiencies in both zinc and magnesium, although its effectiveness is less conclusive for those who are not deficient.

TRY 5 ISSUES FOR JUST £5

Be at the top of your game all year round – claim 5 issues of *Men's Fitness* for £5

Photographer: Joel Anderson

Visit **dennismags.co.uk/mensfitness** or call **0844 844 0081**

For **PRINT + DIGITAL** quote offer code: **G2015BMB** or for **PRINT ONLY** quote offer code: **G2015PMB**

Calls will cost 7p per minute plus your telephone company's access charge.